WONDERS
OF
SCIENCE

Simplified

A WONDERFUL SET OF OPTICAL ILLUSIONS

Here are some remarkable optical illusions. In 1 the two black discs in the centre are the same size, although the right-hand one looks larger than the left. In 2 all the horizontal lines are the same length. In 3 if we rotate this page the spiral and the circle will look as if they were moving round. In 4 the dotted circles are the same size, although the bottom one looks larger. In 5 we misjudge the continuation of the slanting line. In 6 the rectangles are upright, but they seem toppling over. No. 7, looked at from a distance, appears as a series of white hexagons. In 8 we seem first to be looking down on the cube, and then up under it. In 9, 10, 11, 13, 18, 20, 21 and 22 parallel lines appear curved or slanting. In 12, 14 and 16 the triangle, circle and squares appear warped. No. 15 appears as a series of spirals, but really consists of circles. In 17 and 19 we appear to be first looking up and then down upon the blocks and stairs

WONDERS

OF

SCIENCE

Simplified

▼▼▼▼▼▼▼▼▼▼▼▼▼▼▼▼▼▼▼▼▼▼▼▼▼▼▼▼▼▼▼

THREE VOLUMES
IN ONE

▲▲▲▲▲▲▲▲▲▲▲▲▲▲▲▲▲▲▲▲▲▲▲▲▲▲▲▲▲

METRO PUBLICATIONS

NEW YORK

PUBLISHED 1943 BY METRO PUBLICATIONS

70 FIFTH AVENUE, NEW YORK

PRINTED IN UNITED STATES OF AMERICA

Contents

HOW YOU CAN SEE THROUGH A BRICK

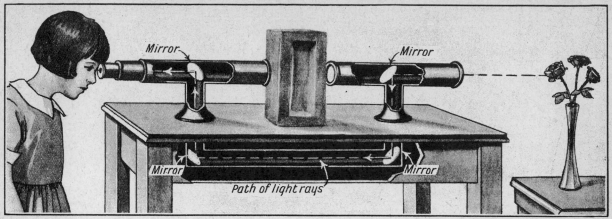

There is a familiar saying that you cannot see through a brick wall, but here is a way in which you can, at any rate, see what is on the other side of a brick and appear to be looking through it. On the table are two telescope-like tubes, and when you look into the eye-piece you see quite clearly what is on the other side of the brick, although it is hidden when you look without the telescope. The stands of the two tubes are continued under the table and linked together by another tube. Four mirrors are arranged at angles, as seen, and the object looked at—in this case a vase of flowers—is reflected from mirror to mirror, so that what the observer really sees is not the flowers themselves, but the reflection of the flowers in one of the mirrors.

THINGS THAT ARE NOT WHAT THEY SEEM

Appearances are often deceptive, and here are some remarkable examples. The legs of the men in the middle picture do not appear straight, but if you hold the picture horizontally and look along the legs you will see that actually they are straight. Similarly, the figures in the top left-hand corner do not appear circles; they seem to be ellipses. You will find they are circles if you test them with compasses. In both cases the eye is distracted by the plaid pattern. Look at the two figures in the bottom right-hand corner. Who would think they were the same size? Yet they are. Their position deceives the eye. In the bottom left-hand corner are some black squares separated by white lines. As you look at these the angles where the lines cross appear to be grey. In the right-hand top figure we seem to be looking down upon three cubes, but after a minute or two our vision appears to change and we are looking up at them.

Volume I

WONDERS OF NATURE

Contents—Volume I. Wonders of Nature

BOOK 1. THE HISTORY AND MYSTERY OF ASTRONOMY

BOOK 2. THE ODDEST PHENOMENA ON EARTH

BOOK 3. WATCHING THE PHYSICAL WORLD CHANGE

BOOK 4. SECRETS OF THE WEATHER SIMPLIFIED

BOOK 5. THROUGH THE WONDERLAND OF NATURE

Book 1

▼▼▼▼▼▼▼▼▼▼▼▼▼▼

The HISTORY
and MYSTERY
of ASTRONOMY

▲▲▲▲▲▲▲▲▲▲▲▲▲▲

HOW WE ALL DEPEND ON THE ASTRONOMER

Many people must have asked themselves "Of what use is astronomy? What good can it be to mankind to know the weight of Jupiter, for instance?" Yet the patient, never-ceasing work of the astronomer is of vital importance to us every day of our lives, did we but know it. In the following chapter we learn some remarkable facts about the astronomer and his wonderful work in the great observatories of the world, many of which are situated on high and lonely mountains.

IT might be thought that astronomy, the study of the heavens, was not of much use to ordinary people. But, in fact, it is of very great importance, not merely to a few men of science but to all of us, in our daily lives. For instance, without astronomy it would be impossible for us to keep our clocks and watches accurate : nor would the sailor be able to guide his ship accurately from port to port. He would have to waste much time if his knowledge, acquired from the astronomer, of the Sun, the stars and the planets did not help him on his way, and waste of time would be waste of money, so that all the goods we buy from overseas would cost us more

Astronomy also helps us with past time as well as with the present, for we can check a date in history by, say, the record of an eclipse.

The discovery of that wonderful element helium, the gas which can be used to lift airships and does not catch fire, was made by astronomers. They found it in the sun just over a quarter of a century before it was discovered on the earth If helium gas had been used in the ill-fated airship R101, the terrible disaster which we all remember would never have overtaken it ; the airship would not have been burned

Good Work for Mankind

The astronomer, then, is a man who is doing much good work for mankind. He has to work very hard, and usually for a small reward. The work in a big observatory, such as that at Greenwich or the Lick Observatory in California, is carefully divided up among the various members of the staff, just as it might be in a big factory. The astronomers work in shifts both day and night. As one of them goes off duty his colleague comes on.

He lies down on a mattress beneath the eyepiece of a big telescope, which is kept fixed by a special motor on the particular star or planet under observation. But for the motor the

earth as it rolled round on its axis, carrying the observatory with it, would soon move the telescope out of range of the object on which it was fixed.

The famous Lick Observatory on top of Mount Hamilton, California, where, with giant telescopes, astronomers have made many marvellous discoveries in the heavens

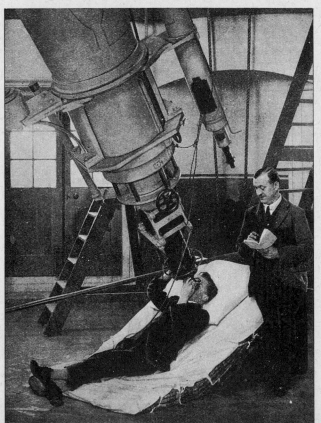

How the astronomer watches the heavens through the great 28-inch telescope at Greenwich Observatory

Very often the astronomer has to put up with considerable discomfort from stiffness and from cold, for the problem of heating an observatory is a very difficult one. This is because any current of warm air would cause the atmosphere round the lens to quiver, as we see it do on a hot day in the summer, and this would make accurate observation impossible.

It is interesting to recall that Caroline Herschel, sister of Sir William Herschel, the famous astronomer who did such wonderful pioneer work with the telescope, used to sit for long hours in the open air assisting her brother with his records till her fingers became numb with cold. Sometimes the very ink froze in the bottle she was holding in her hand.

The astronomer has to keep his attention fixed not only on the stars but also on a number of complicated instruments which record his observations and check the knowledge he has helped to accumulate. Tremendous mathematical calculations have also to be made, while there is always the danger lest a cloud obscure the sky and spoil the night's work.

Up in the Mountains

It is in order to take advantage of the purest atmosphere that so many observatories are built on high mountains. On these bleak heights the astronomer, far removed from the rest of the world, spends an arduous life matching his tiny brain against the enormous problems of the universe, so that man's knowledge and power may be increased.

So we see that the astronomer is not merely a man who pursues a rather expensive hobby. One of his greatest services to us all is the removal of the doubts and fears which formerly troubled mankind. At one time an eclipse was thought a terrible thing, perhaps foretelling the end of the world, while comets were supposed to bring plagues and other disasters in their wake. Now, thanks to the astronomer, we know better.

THE SIGNS OF THE ZODIAC AND THEIR STARS

VERY early in the history of man it was noticed that the Sun in its annual journey seemed to pass across a band of the heavens in which were twelve groups of stars. These groups of stars we call constellations, a long word from the Latin which simply means " stars together."

Just as we look into the fire and fancy we see pictures, so the Ancients looked at these groups of stars and fancied they saw people, animals and other objects in them. They therefore gave the groups the names of these fancied objects. Sometimes they are called by their Latin names, and

In the picture on this page we see the various constellations, but it is difficult for us to recognise any likeness in them to the objects named. We see also the usual kind of picture which represents each constellation, the names in Latin and English, the date on which the Sun enters each constellation, and

in the two strokes representing the twins, the wavy lines representing water, and the arrow for the archer.

The twelve constellations that have been named form a narrow zone or band round the heavens, and this is known as the Zodiac, from two Greek words which mean " the circle of little animals." The band is divided into twelve equal parts, which are known as the Signs of the Zodiac, and it is clear, therefore, that as the constellations are of different sizes they overlap to some extent in the equal divisions. This can be seen plainly in the outer ring of the diagram.

The constellations of the Zodiac, with their principal stars and their symbols

sometimes by their English names, as follows: Aries, the Ram ; Taurus, the Bull ; Gemini, the Twins ; Cancer, the Crab ; Leo, the Lion ; Virgo, the Virgin ; Libra, the Scales ; Scorpio, the Scorpion ; Sagittarius, the Archer ; Capricornus, the Goat ; Aquarius, the Water-Carrier ; and Pisces, the Fishes. There is a simple rhyme which will help us to remember them.

> The Ram, the Bull, the Heavenly Twins,
> And, next the Crab, the Lion shines,
>   The Virgin and the Scales ;
> The Scorpion, Archer and He-goat,
> The Man that has the Water-pot,
>   And Fish with shining scales.

some queer signs which are often used to save the trouble of giving the full name or drawing a picture. These are a kind of hieroglyphic, and in some of them we can see a rough resemblance to what they represent, as, for example,

When the Sun appears to be in one of the Signs of the Zodiac, as, for example, the Archer, on January 1st, neither that constellation nor the neighbouring ones can be seen, because they are in the sky at daytime.

It is supposed that there are references in the Bible to the Signs of the Zodiac, some scholars thinking that Mazzaroth in the 38th chapter of Job, verse 32, refers to this band of constellations, and the reference to the Sun's circuit in the 19th Psalm, verse 6, is also regarded as a reference to the Zodiac. The men of the Bible were, we know, great students of the heavens.

HOW MEN USED TO THINK OF EARTH AND SKY

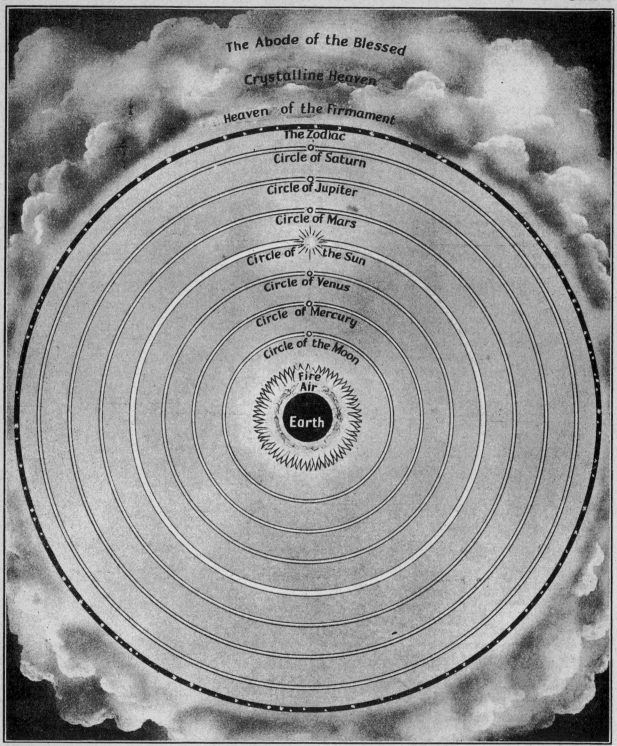

The Abode of the Blessed

Crystalline Heaven

Heaven of the Firmament

The Zodiac

Circle of Saturn

Circle of Jupiter

Circle of Mars

Circle of the Sun

Circle of Venus

Circle of Mercury

Circle of the Moon

Fire
Air
Earth

Hundreds of years ago men of science had very incorrect ideas about the Earth on which we live and the sky above us with its twinkling points of light. In this picture we see the Earth and heavens as conceived by the great Greek philosopher, Aristotle, and his ideas held the field for centuries. The Earth was supposed to occupy the centre of the universe, and round it was a sea of air. Outside this was a region of fire, and then the various heavenly bodies like the Moon, the planets and the Sun circled in heavens of their own. Beyond these bodies was the heaven of the firmament which contained the Zodiac, or twelve constellations, shown on page 11. Then came a crystalline heaven, and finally the heaven which was regarded as the abode of the blessed. On the page opposite we see the true idea of the universe, which is based not on theory or fancy but on actual observation

AN ACTUAL PHOTOGRAPH OF THE UNIVERSE

The Sun would appear as a point of light in the Milky Way

We now know that the Earth, so far from being the centre of the universe, is merely a tiny planet belonging to one of countless myriads of suns that are gathered into island universes and scattered throughout the vastness of Space. Our Earth and Sun belong to the Milky Way system, part of which is shown here in a photograph taken at Harvard College Observatory, and given by courtesy of that institution. If an astronomer could go to a point millions of millions of miles away in distant Space, and, with a giant telescope and camera, photograph our Sun, it would appear merely as a tiny point of light amid myriads of other similar points, all of which would be globes of fire, some larger and some smaller than our Sun. The Earth and planets would, of course, be too small to be seen at all

HOW THE SOLAR SYSTEM ORIGINATED

Rings of matter thrown off by Sun and condensing into planets

No one can say for certain how the Solar System originated, but scientists have tried to solve the problem. Laplace, the great French astronomer, supposed that there was once a great cloud of fiery gas that under the action of its own gravitation became globular and rotated. As the gas cooled, it contracted and rotated more and more rapidly, becoming flatter till at last centrifugal force threw off ring after ring. Finally, each ring broke up and its material collected into a planet. In the same way the rotating planets threw off moons

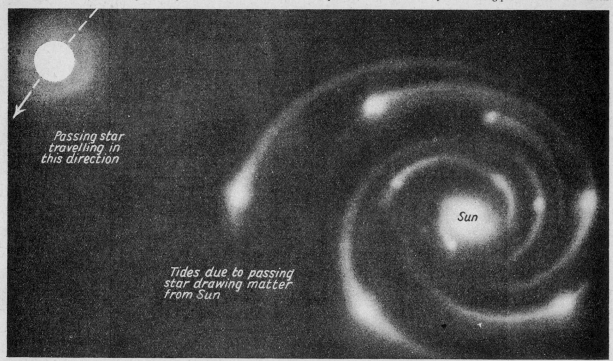

Passing star travelling in this direction

Tides due to passing star drawing matter from Sun

Laplace's theory of how the Solar System originated was accepted for more than a century, but as knowledge of the Sun and planets grew it was recognised that there were tremendous objections to it. For one thing, if it were true the outer planets, Pluto, Neptune, Uranus and Saturn, would be the oldest worlds, while the inner ones like Mercury, Venus, the Earth, and Mars would be the newest. We know now that this is not the case. The generally accepted view of the Solar System now held is that in some far-distant age, when the System was a huge fiery volume of gas a star approached causing great tides which drew off masses of the gas. The whole system revolved as a spiral, but ultimately the various detached masses cooled down and at last became the planets

WHAT HAPPENS IN A TOTAL ECLIPSE OF THE SUN

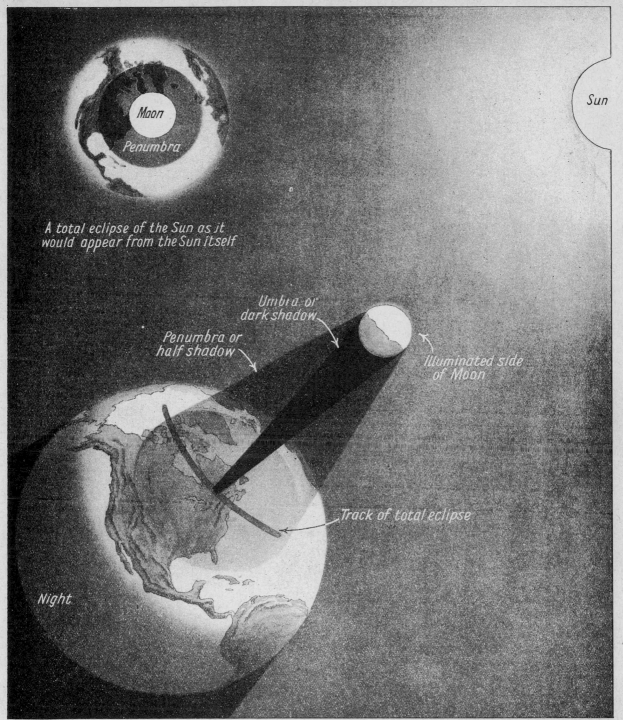

Moon

Penumbra

A total eclipse of the Sun as it would appear from the Sun itself

Sun

Umbra or dark shadow

Penumbra or half shadow

Illuminated side of Moon

Track of total eclipse

Night

Here we see a total eclipse of the Sun. The Moon in its journey gets between the Sun and the Earth, and when we look up we see what appears to be a black shadow creeping across the Sun's face. Of course, it is not a shadow at all, but actually the Moon itself, which looks black in contrast with the Sun's brilliance. As the Moon continues on its journey and the Earth goes on rotating on its axis, the shadow cast by the Moon on the Earth as it gets in the way of the sunlight travels in a line across the Earth's surface. If the Sun were only a point of light there would be nothing but the dark shadow, but as the Sun has so large a surface there is also a wide zone on the Earth's surface where a partial shadow is caused by part of the Sun's light. It is called the penumbra, or "almost shadow," in contrast to the "umbra" or shadow itself. Along this zone the eclipse is not total but only partial. We can make a penumbra by lighting two candles to represent the two opposite edges of the Sun, placing them fairly near together at equal distances from a wall, and observing the shadow they cast on the wall from an orange held in the way. On either side of the dark shadow there will be a penumbra made by the light of only one candle. In the top left-hand corner we see the Earth during a total eclipes as it would appear from the Sun

THE ENORMOUS SIZE OF SOME STARS

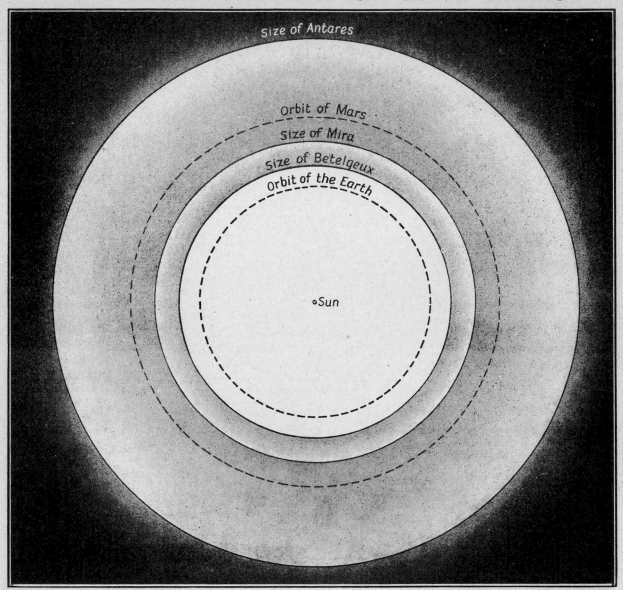

By means of a wonderful instrument known as the interferometer, some of the distant stars have been measured, and truly astonishing are the results, as we can see in this picture-diagram showing some of the stars with the Sun and the orbits of the Earth and Mars drawn to the same scale. It will be seen that some of the stars measured are much bigger in diameter than the Earth's orbit, while one of them is not only bigger than the orbit of Mars, but more than twice as great in diameter as the Earth's orbit. Antares, the chief star in the constellation of the Scorpion is the biggest star that has been measured so far. Stars vary much in size but not in mass, and consequently their densities must be very different. The densities of the stars vary from several times that of iron to one-millionth that of water. It is difficult for us to imagine matter so enormously drawn out

If the planets are arranged in their right order there is a remarkable sequence of size. They fit into a figure shaped like a cigar, and the suggestion of scientists is that some star passing our Sun in the past drew out some of its substance, which cooled into the planets

THE PLANET MARS AND ITS STRANGE MARKINGS

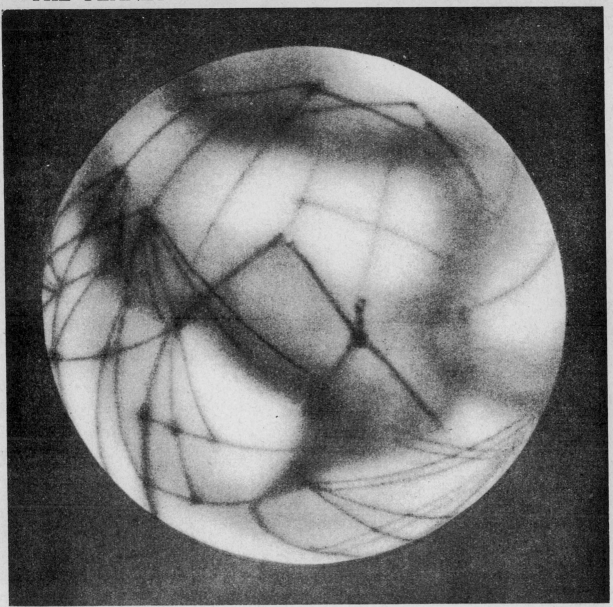

The planet Mars is the most interesting of all the Sun's family of worlds, for we are able to see its surface with some distinctness, this not being shut off from our view by dense clouds, as in the case of some of the other planets. Mars shows us a more or less ruddy disc, and for this reason it is often called "the red planet." There are white patches at the planet's poles, which are known as the "polar caps," and are supposed to be masses of snow or ice, or possibly frozen carbon-dioxide. In the planet's summer these become smaller, and then certain lines seen all over the surface become more distinct. Some astronomers have supposed that the lines are water channels or "canals" made by intelligent beings, and that their increased distinctness at certain seasons is due to vegetation

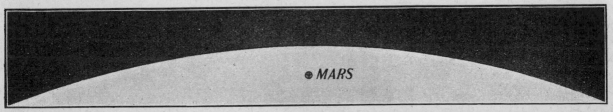

● *MARS*

Mars is very small compared with the Sun, as can be seen in this picture-diagram, which shows the planet as a round dot on a part of the Sun's disc drawn to scale. Mars at its greatest distance is 154,860,000 miles from the Sun, and at its shortest distance 128,440,000 miles. While the Sun is 867,000 miles in diameter, Mars is only 4,352 miles or little more than half the diameter of the Earth

In Germany and America many big cities have what is known as a planetarium. It is a circular building with a dome, on the inside of which a wonderful projector throws points of light to represent the various stars in the sky. The projector, which is certainly one of the wonders of the world, is operated by clockwork and moves the points of light in the same way as the stars move in the sky. The movements can be speeded up or slowed down, and it is possible to see in an hour the movements of the stars and planets for a year

Book 2

▼▼▼▼▼▼▼▼▼▼▼

The ODDEST

PHENOMENA

on EARTH

▲▲▲▲▲▲▲▲▲▲▲

THE IMPRESSIVE NATURAL BRIDGE OF ARGENTINA

Here is one of the most massive natural bridges in the world. It is to be seen spanning the Mendoza River which rises on the eastern flank of Aconcagua, the great volcano in the Andes 22,860 feet high. The bridge, sculptured out of the solid rock, is known as the Bridge of the Inca, and was at one time supposed to have been the work of the ancient inhabitants of these parts. But it is now known to be wholly a product of nature and to have been sculptured by the swiftly flowing waters of the river aided by the power of the Sun and wind. The scenery all round for miles is very majestic, the towering mountains forming a wonderful background to the bridge

NATURE AS A GREAT BRIDGE-BUILDER

Natural bridges as striking as any bridge made by the skill of man are to be seen in many parts of the world.
In some cases they are of imposing dimensions and form a most impressive feature of the landscape.
Here we read something about these natural bridges and the way in which they have been formed

THE sculpturing of the rocks by Nature produces many fantastic forms, and perhaps nowhere are there so many varieties as on the American continent, both North and South. Vast chasms are carved out of the solid rock by rivers like the Colorado, the canyons of which, in some places, are a mile deep ; and wind and sand sculpture also provide many remarkable forms.

In the Garden of the Gods, in Colorado, there are 500 acres covered with rocky towers and spires that look against the skyline as though they were the tops of cathedrals built by the hand of man. An example of this kind of natural sculpture is to be seen in the photograph taken in Bryce Canyon

But of all these interesting geological forms none is more striking or remarkable than the great natural bridges that have been carved out and stand up so imposingly often hundreds of feet above the river or ground below.

America seems to be the great land of natural bridges. The most famous is that near Lexington in Virginia, which is 200 feet high, but there are many not only far higher than this, but of much more imposing proportions. The examples given on this page and the previous page will give some idea of how majestic these rocky formations may be.

All natural bridges are not formed in the same way. Some have been formed by earthquakes, the rock underneath having been shaken away, leaving a mass suspended.

Other natural bridges have resulted from disintegration by water and wind, and the falling away of cliffs and rocks through the cracking and breaking up of the strata. A layer of harder rock above is left in position, and so we have a natural bridge.

But the most common way in which these bridges are formed is by the work of an underground river passing through limestone caverns. The cavern is made by the water that percolates through the soil above, dissolving the carbonate of lime.

The waters meet underground and form a subterranean river. This perhaps flows down to a lower cave and wears away a new and lower bed for itself. Then part of the cave roof falls in, so that the river is open to the sky, but another part of the roof is left suspended, and this forms a natural bridge.

In the course of time the river itself may be diverted, but not until it has worn away its bed so that this is two or three hundred feet below the bridge.

It is perhaps not at all surprising that where these formations exist among primitive and ignorant peoples they are regarded as of supernatural origin.

A marvellous natural bridge of rock 300 feet high in San Juan County, Utah. It is, from its shape, called the Rainbow National Bridge

THE WATER'S FANTASTIC WORK IN A CAVE

The limestone caves found in many parts of the world are often on a huge scale, so that in some places they have not yet been completely explored. These are the work of running water, which dissolves the limestone. Sometimes the roof of the cave falls in. Dripping water when it evaporates leaves stalactites on the roof and stalagmites on the floor of the cave. In some cases the work of the water produces strange results. Here is a photograph of what is known as the Monument Mountain and Rothrocks Cathedral in Wyandotte Cave, Indiana. The so-called mountain consists of huge stalagmites around which fragments of the fallen roof of the cave have gathered, giving a cathedral-like effect. The "mountain" is 175 feet high, and the cave in which it is found is 225 feet high, and a quarter of a mile round. Hanging over the "spire" of the "cathedral" are stalactites

Here is another fantastic effect brought about by running water in the Luray Cavern in Virginia. This cave underlies an area in the foothills of the Blue Ridge Mountains, and is of vast size. It contains numerous galleries rising one above another to a height of nearly 300 feet, and as can be seen here, the stalactites and stalagmites are on a huge scale. When the cave is lighted the limestone formation sparkles and makes the place like a veritable fairyland. It is strange that the water after carving out the cave should then begin to fill it up again with these massive formations. Some caves are almost completely filled with stalactites and stalagmites

WATER AS A DESTROYER AND REBUILDER

The beauties and curious formations of some of the limestone caves are almost past belief, and the strange forms which their stalactites and stalagmites take are as varied as the forms of the snow crystals. Some facts about the destructive power of water and its ability to rebuild where it has broken down are told on this page

WATER has an enormous power as a destroyer of even the hardest rocks, and it is equally effective as a rebuilder.

We see this particularly in limestone caves, which in some parts of the world are of enormous dimensions. The Mammoth Cave of Kentucky, for instance, covers many miles, and has never been entirely explored. It contains vast chambers, long tunnels and passages, and rivers and lakes, and all the excavation has been performed by the water.

In some places after the underground water has eaten away great sections of the rock and formed large caves, the roofs have fallen in, leaving a chasm like the Cheddar Gorge or a large hole known to scientists as a sink-hole or limestone sink. Sometimes the roof falls as a result of the weakening of its supports and sometimes the water wears away the rock more gradually, and causes it to crumble.

Water Work

In the Karst region at the head of the Adriatic Sea the whole landscape has been changed by the action of the water on the limestone rock of the district.

The solvent action of the water before and after it sinks through the ground has made the region very uneven. There are short gullies, large ravines, and deep valleys in the lime-

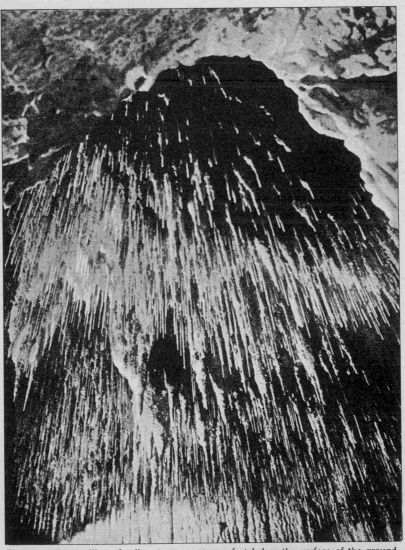

stone, and these often end abruptly and discharge their waters into caves and subterranean tunnels. Sink-holes abound, and are in many cases hundreds of feet deep. The slopes everywhere are very steep, and so striking is the whole scene as a result of the destructive action of the water that it has given a scientific name to scenery of the same kind elsewhere, which is known as Karst topography.

But what the water takes away it gives back, and we find in limestone caves extensive stalactites and stalagmites, or icicles of rock, some pendant and some erect, built up of rock that has been returned by the water.

Water percolating through the limestone becomes charged with dissolved carbonate of lime. Then when it finds its way to the roof of a cave it gives up some of the rock as it evaporates and a stalactite is the result. When the water collects on the roof so slowly as to evaporate entirely before a drop can form, the whole of the carbonate of lime that was dissolved will be left adhering to the roof.

Slow Deposit

Evaporation is most rapid near the margins and over the centre of each drop as it develops, and the deposit that is left takes the form of small white rings. A stalactite, therefore, grows outward.

When the water comes through the roof too rapidly to evaporate entirely there, some falls to the floor and, spattering as it strikes the rocks, builds up a thick cone known as a stalagmite.

Some caves are almost filled up with stalactites and stalagmites, so effectually does the water build up what it had previously destroyed.

The marvellous ceiling of a limestone cave 3,000 feet below the surface of the ground. The cave is to be seen at Domanova in Czecho-Slovakia and the roof, as can be seen in the photograph, is one mass of sparkling stalactites

THE GREATEST FOREST ON THE EARTH'S SURFACE

So dense is the great Amazon forest of South America, that man is helpless in trying to fight against the rank, luxuriant vegetation. If by dint of great labour he clears a space to-day, it is almost literally true that it is overgrown again to-morrow. Thousands of square miles have never been explored by the white man, and the only way great sections of its dense region can be seen is from the air. Here we see an aeroplane that took photographs of the Amazon forest flying over the region on a cloudy day

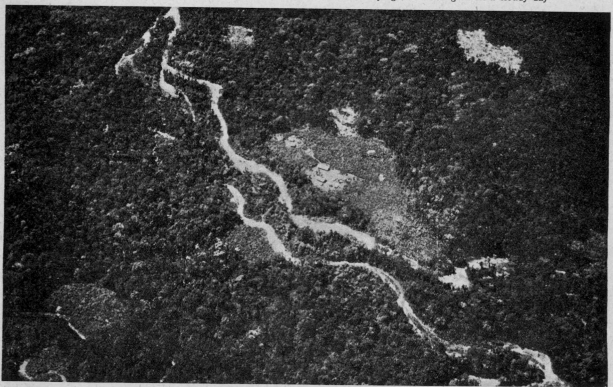

This photograph gives some idea of the denseness of the great Amazon forest. It was taken from the air by the aeroplane seen in the upper picture. The river that can be seen winding its way through the forest is the Asupisu, one of the tributaries of the mighty Amazon, and the buildings shown in the clearing are Government rest houses, placed there for the use of travellers. Clearings of this kind involve an immense amount of work, for if they are unattended, in a few days they become overgrown once more with a dense vegetation

THE MIGHTY FOREST OF SOUTH AMERICA

The Amazon forest and the mighty Amazon river are certainly two of the greatest natural wonders of the world. Nowhere else, not even in the dense African forest, is vegetation so luxuriant as in this immense area of tropical South America. The forest is 200 miles wide along the Atlantic coast and reaches to the snow-capped Andes in an ever widening band. Here are some interesting facts about this wonderful forest

In the great Amazon forest of South America vegetation is king. It takes control of an area, thousands of square miles in extent and man is helpless when he tries to compete with the luxuriant plant life that grows so rapidly as almost to be seen advancing like an invading army.

Any patch of ground or trail cleared to-day is overgrown again to-morrow, and one may move for days and even weeks in this dense forest and scarcely see the daylight which is all but shut out by the thick canopy of leaves overhead.

Nowhere else in the world is plant-life so rich and crowded. Every type of plant is represented and any single acre contains scores of species. The trees rise like great poles with their first branches high up above the ground as they struggle to reach the sunshine, and these trees are the props for all kinds of creepers that in their turn fight their way up to the sunlight. Many of the trees in order to obtain the necessary support have buttressed trunks, and in many parts where rain is plentiful tree ferns give an appearance such as the coal forests of past ages must have borne.

A profusion of flowers rich in colour and beautiful in form is found in this marvellous forest, varying according to the particular area which may be explored. The forest lies wholly within the tropics, but owing to the varying altitudes, plants of almost all climates are found somewhere.

The whole forest is irrigated by the greatest river-system in the world, that of the Amazon, and its hundreds of tributaries, which have been described as not so much a river as a gigantic reservoir. The main river extends from the sea to the foot of the Andes, and in the rainy season varies in width from five miles to four hundred.

It is estimated that one fourth of all the fresh water in the world is concentrated in the Amazon river system and the fresh water pours out for 200 miles into the sea.

The forest ranges from mangrove swamps in the coastal regions to bush country where the naturalist Agassiz counted 117 different kinds of trees in half a square mile of ground. Thousands of square miles have never been explored by the white man.

In this photograph we see part of the huge Amazon forest with one of the tributaries of the Amazon river, the Pachitea, meandering among the trees with the many islands formed by the winding of the waters. The Amazon, with its tributaries, is the greatest fresh-water system in the world, and the area drained is about two and a half million square miles. Nearly two thousand different kinds of fish live in the Amazon, including the strange electric eel which stuns its prey with a powerful electric shock

WHY THE GEYSER ERUPTS AT INTERVALS

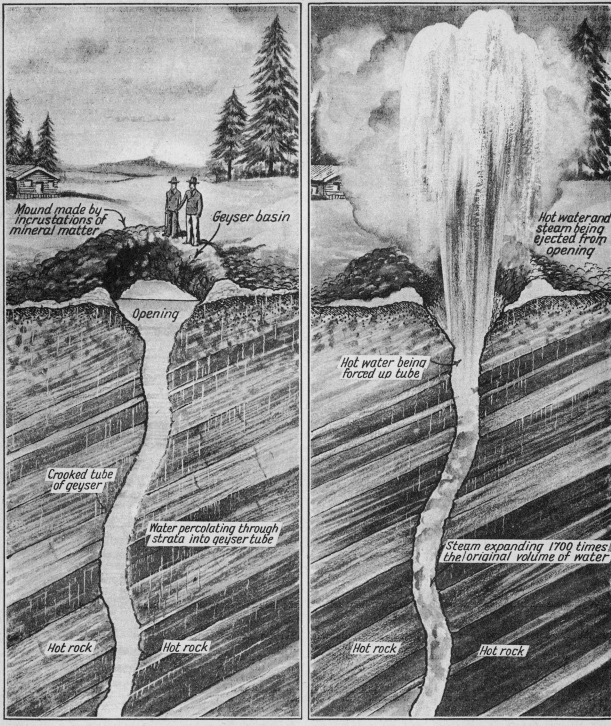

Mound made by incrustations of mineral matter

Geyser basin

Opening

Crooked tube of geyser

Water percolating through strata into geyser tube

Hot rock

Hot rock

Hot water and steam being ejected from opening

Hot water being forced up tube

Steam expanding 1700 times the original volume of water

Hot rock

Hot rock

Geysers are hot springs from which boiling water and steam are hurled, at more or less regular intervals, to a height sometimes of over 200 feet. A geyser has an opening called the geyser tube leading down to unknown depths in the Earth. Round the opening at the top there is a shallow basin, which is often filled with warm water, and frequently inside it round the opening is a mound. The basin and mound are composed of mineral matter, generally silica, left behind when the water evaporates, for the hot water of a geyser always contains a large quantity of mineral matter in solution. It is believed that water which has percolated through the ground enters the geyser tube just as it does a well, and that, far down, the walls of the tube are of hot rock. Here the water is brought to boiling-point, and is converted into steam, expanding about 1,700 times its original bulk. When steam forms in a kettle of boiling water the steam can rise and escape, but in a geyser tube, which is long and narrow, and often crooked, the steam formed far down is unable to escape quickly enough, and so its expansion hurls out the water above. Then there is a quiet period, till the same operation is repeated

SPOUTING FOUNTAINS OF BOILING WATER

Geysers are hot springs in which the boiling water and steam are ejected violently from the opening, and here we read how this curious natural phenomenon operates. The finest geysers in the world are found in the United States, New Zealand and Iceland. In the Yellowstone National Park alone there are more than a hundred active geysers. One of them, known as Old Faithful, sends up its water at almost hourly periods

IN certain regions of the Earth, generally in lands which are subject to volcanic upheavals, there are hot springs that eject boiling water sometimes to a great height. The water is in many cases shot out at fairly regular intervals, so that people know almost to the minute when the eruption will occur. Sometimes this can be speeded up by the simple process of throwing a stone down the mouth of the geyser.

A geyser consists of a long, narrow tube reaching from an opening above ground to some unknown depth in the crust of the Earth. It is often not straight, but very crooked, and it goes down to regions where the rocks are hot. Water percolates through the soil and strata and finds its way by cracks and fissures into the geyser tube, so that this becomes filled with water that gets warmed by convection.

In other words, the hot rock below raises the temperature of the water and gradually by the hot water rising and the cooler water flowing in the whole contents of the geyser tube is raised to a high temperature.

Great Heat

Near the top the water is often 180 to 190 degrees Fahrenheit. Then suddenly there is a burst, and up shoots a column of steam and boiling water, sometimes to a height of 200 feet or more. After a minute or two the eruption ceases, and all is quiet till the next eruption. Sometimes the water issuing from the pipe may have a temperature of 250 degrees Fahrenheit.

What happens is this: the water at the bottom of the tube in contact with the hot rocks gets warmer and warmer, till at last steam is formed.

But in the geyser, owing to the great length of the tube and its relative narrowness, the steam is unable to escape fast enough, and being expanded to 1,700 times its former bulk, it hurls out the water above, and thus we see steam and water shot from the geyser's mouth.

The boiling water that comes out is at a temperature higher than 212 degrees Fahrenheit, because when it was below there was the pressure of the column of water above it, and water under pressure boils at higher temperatures than when the pressure is less.

That is why on a high mountain water boils at very much less than 212 degrees Fahrenheit. At the top of Mont Blanc, for instance, it boils at 183 degrees Fahrenheit, and at the top of Everest at 160 degrees Fahrenheit. Even at the summit of Snowdon water will boil at 206 degrees Fahrenheit.

When the water has been ejected by the eruption the geyser settles down

stone or clod of earth into the geyser's mouth. The solid object interferes with the convection or upward circulation of the warm water in the tube, and thus holds the hot water down where it is being heated. This helps it to reach a boiling temperature sooner than it would do in the ordinary way.

Soap is sometimes placed in the mouth of a geyser, and this hastens the eruption, because anything which thickens the water reduces the convection and operates in the way already described.

Of course, all geysers do not shoot the column of water up to great heights like 200 or 250 feet. There are some which erupt only a small column of water to a height of a few feet, doing this every few minutes, and it is possible that the differences in the behaviour of geysers are the result of different conditions or, in other words, that there are several explanations of the eruptions that take place.

New Geysers

In the Yellowstone National Park of America some geysers have died out within the last thirty years. The reason is that the geyser water is constantly cooling the hot rock, and in time this ceases to be hot enough to boil the water. On the other hand, new geysers have come into existence in the same region during the period named.

It is not surprising that these striking wonders of Nature have fired the poet's imagination:

The basin and opening of one of the geysers in the Yellowstone Park

quietly, and nothing happens till the next outburst, when again the column of boiling water and steam is hurled from the opening.

While these eruptions occur at more or less regular intervals in many geysers, the outbursts can be expedited, as already explained, by throwing a

I'm the Dragon's Mouth, the geyser—
Mother Earth, we do despise her.
Come not near me !
Can't you hear me ?
E'en the beasts and wild birds fear me !
Down within me hear me roaring,
Hear my tumult and my snoring,
Belching forth with mud and sulphur—
Mother Earth I would engulf her.

THE WORLD'S POPULATION IN A BIG BOX

When we hear that the world's population at the present time consists of two thousand million men, women and children, we think this is an enormous crowd and that it is quite beyond our powers to visualise such a gathering. Dr. Hendrik Van Loon has given us a very graphic idea of what this number of people means and shows us that, compared with the size of the world in which we live, it is small. The whole of the human race, says Dr. Van Loon, could easily be packed into a box measuring half a mile in each direction "Balance it over the Grand Canyon of Arizona," he continues, "and tell a little dachshund to give it a push. A century from now a little mound densely covered with vegetable matter would perhaps indicate where humanity lay buried, and that would be all." This picture will help us to visualise in how very small a space the whole human race could be packed   The canyon is nearly a mile deep and the half-mile cubical box is drawn to scale

A RIVER'S MARVELLOUS ROCK SCULPTURE

The Canyon of the Colorado, that is the chasm that this river has cut out for itself in the solid rock is one of the natural wonders of the world.   If the canyon did not exist we should never believe that the excavating power of running water was so great.   Here are some interesting facts about this wonder

Nowhere else in the world is there such a marvellous example of the power of running water in carving out a bed for itself and sculpturing the rocks, as in the basin of the Colorado river.

This river drains a vast plateau which extends from the western side of the Rocky Mountains to the head of the Gulf of California, and for nearly 500 miles it flows at the bottom of a gorge that varies from three to six thousand feet in depth.   In other words, the river has, at places, carved out for itself a bed more than a mile deep in the rock.

But it has done more than dig a narrow gorge.   It has sculptured the whole of the plateau into terraces like courses of titanic masonry.   In many places there are really two canyons, the upper one being several miles wide, with vast lines of cliff walls and a broad plain between them, in which runs the second canyon, a deep and narrow gorge with the river at the bottom.

It has been said that a hunter might shoot a stag across the chasm, but it would take him more than a day's journey to get the venison.   So carved and cut up is the whole country that it can scarcely be crossed except by birds and aeroplanes.

Professor Bonney tells us that the formation of these vast gorges has been rendered possible by a combination of favourable circumstances.   The whole plateau is built up of masses of fairly hard sandstone and limestone with but little of softer materials, disposed horizontally with curious regularity, like courses of masonry ;   and it rests on a foundation of solid granite into which sometimes the river has cut a trench for as much as a thousand feet.

The rainfall in the immediate neighbourhood is slight, so that the elements can do little to destroy the edges of the trench and diminish the steepness of the walls ;   but the rain is heavy on the head-waters of the river, for such a work as this could only be done by powerful cutting tools.

"It is impossible," says Mr. George Wharton James, an authority on the subject, "to conceive what the Canyon is from the descriptions or pictures.   One's most extravagant expectatio s are indefinitely surpassed, though one expects much from what is said of it 'as the biggest chasm on earth'."

The titanic masonry of the Canyon of the Colorado, where the river has cut a chasm over a mile deep through sandstone and granite

A MARVELLOUS MOUNTAIN OF SOLID SALT

In the south of Palestine there is a mountain composed entirely of rock salt and as we might suppose it is on the shores of the Dead Sea. Indeed, it owes its origin to the Dead Sea, that strangest and lowest of all the world's lakes.

This salt sea has an area of 360 square miles, and while in the south it is only from 3 to 30 feet deep, in the north it reaches a depth of 1,310 feet, or a quarter of a mile. Its mean depth is 1,080 feet.

The Dead Sea lies in a hollow, and its surface is 1,300 feet below that of the Mediterranean Sea. The level varies a good deal at different times of the year, being sometimes 15 feet lower than at other periods.

Although the river Jordan pours on an average something like six million tons of water into the Dead Sea every day of the year, the water of this lake gets salter and salter, for the evaporation is great and the river brings much mineral matter down with it.

The mouth of a great cave in the mountain of salt at Usdun, on the Dead Sea in Palestine. The mountain was formerly dissolved in the sea

In past geologic ages the Mediterranean Sea covered Palestine. Then, later on, the land was upheaved and wrinkles formed the mountains of Lebanon, while fractures occurred and parts of the strata slipped forming the rift valley in which are the River Jordan and the Dead Sea.

The Dead Sea became a vast inland sea with a level 1,400 feet higher than at present. But gradually the water evaporated, leaving behind vast deposits of mineral matter that had been in solution, including the great mountain of rock salt shown in the photographs on this page.

The water of the Dead Sea is very salt, far more so than the water of the ocean. While sea-water has from four to six per cent of salts in it, the water of the Dead Sea contains about 25 per cent. In other words, one quarter of the water consists of salt of one kind or another. No wonder it is impossible to sink in it!

This mountain, Jebel Usdun, on the shores of the Dead Sea, is composed of solid rock salt. It is over six miles long and 500 feet high

Book 3

▼▼▼▼▼▼▼▼▼▼▼

WATCHING
the
PHYSICAL
WORLD
CHANGE

▲▲▲▲▲▲▲▲▲▲▲

HOW THE CONTINENTS AND OCEANS WERE FORMED

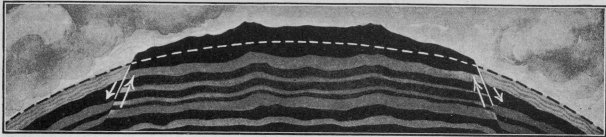

There are various theories as to how the oceans were gathered into basins and the dry land appeared. Five of these theories are shown on this page. Here the rocks have become dislocated, part rising to form a continent and part sinking to form ocean beds

In this diagram the strata instead of being dislocated have become warped, part being pushed up to form a continent, while on either side the rocks have been thrust down to form the ocean beds. The dotted line in all these diagrams represents the original surface

Here we find the same idea as in the top picture, except that while part of the rocks against the faults has been thrust down and thereby becomes ocean beds, the other part has remained stationary in its original position, and not been pushed up as in the top picture

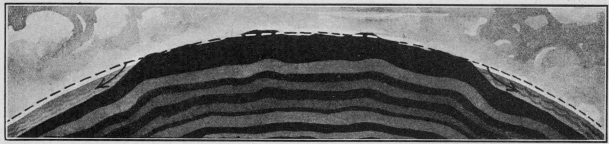

Here is another theory of the scientists. In this case there has been no dislocation of the strata, but they have become warped, and while the part now forming a continent has remained stationary, on either side the rocks have been depressed to form sea beds

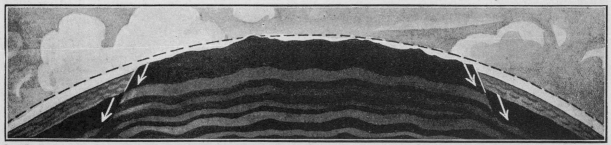

In this picture-diagram we see still another theory explained. Here the rocks after dislocation have all been thrust down beyond the original level, but while the ocean beds have been pushed a considerable distance, the part forming a continent has not moved far

FACTS THAT CHANGE THE LENGTH OF THE DAY

The effect of the tides is to lessen the speed of the Earth's rotation and lengthen the day

The resistance caused by meteorites as they strike the Earth and the fact that they add to its size tend to slow down the speed of rotation

The Earth turns round on its axis in 24 hours, and that is the length of our day. But there are many facts which tend to change the length of the day, some making it longer and some causing it to grow shorter. Here we see two facts that tend to make the day longer

The shrinking of the Earth, making it smaller increases its speed of rotation

The wearing down of the mountain peaks and ranges by wind, water and weather tends to speed up the rotation of the Earth

In this picture we see two facts that tend to speed up the rotation of the Earth and make the day shorter. As the Earth shrinks it gets smaller and the wearing down of the mountain peaks also makes the globe smaller. As it gets smaller it tends to rotate more rapidly

HOW A RIVER CATARACT IS FORMED

Soft sandstone forming bed of river

Hard rock with layer of soft sandstone on top of it

The River Nile would be a much more valuable river for navigation if it were not for the cataracts that occur at various parts of its course. In these pictures we see how a cataract is formed. Originally the bed of the river consisted of a fairly soft rock like sandstone, which the water gradually wore away as it passed over on its way to the sea. Underlying the sandstone was much harder rock

Hard rock projecting above soft sandstone which has been worn away by the water

Gradually in the course of thousands of years more and more of the softer rock on top was worn away, till at last parts of the harder rock, tilted up by movements of the Earth's crust, projected. This hard rock could not be worn away so quickly as the softer layer, and so it continued to project, disturbing the water as it passed over. Gradually a slope was formed down which the river flowed

Hard rock after overlying sandstone is completely worn away, forming cataract

In time all the softer rock was worn away, and the water of the river, being unable to wear down the hard rock, rushed over it in the form of a waterfall. This type of fall is called a cataract, and it is a great hindrance to navigation, for no boat can pass up or down such a section of river. Boats have to be dragged round laboriously or rejoin the river by means of a canal which costs much to construct

THE STRANGE LIFE-STORY OF A RIVER

Rivers, like human beings, have their birth, youth, middle-age and old age.   They are born from a spring or glacier or gully in which storm water collects, and they then flow towards lower levels, cutting out a bed in rock or soil.   At first a river's bed is cut downward, but as time goes on and tributary rivers run into it, while rain and wind sweep over the banks, the bed becomes wider and the banks are worn more and more level.   Here we see in section form the various stages of a river's history

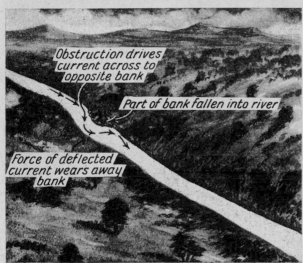

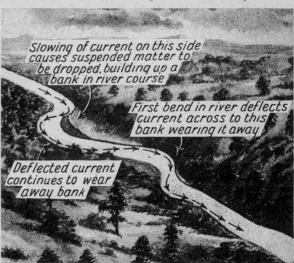

These pictures show how a river begins to meander and form bends as it runs away towards the sea.   On the left is the river in its youth, but a fall of rock or soil on one bank has formed an obstruction throwing the current across to the other bank, which it begins cutting out.   The slowing of the current on the bank where the fall occurred leads to a deposit of matter, and as we see in the right-hand picture, the result is the formation of a curve in the river course

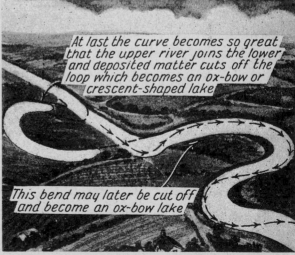

In these two pictures we see further progress in the meandering of a river.   The bend becomes more and more marked till at last the upper and lower reaches of the river meet, and then the deposit of material cuts off the bend, which thus becomes what is known as an ox-bow, or crescent-shaped lake.   Thus the increased meandering at last tends to straighten the river's course once more.   Were it not for the fall of trees and earth from time to time a river would always run straight, because of the inertia of the quickly moving water.   The more sluggish a river is the more likely it is to be turned aside by small obstructions, and once it is diverted from the straight course, as can be seen in these pictures, the curvature increases at an ever-growing rate.   As the convex side of a meander or curve is scoured by the current and the earth is washed away, trees growing on the banks are undermined, and fall outward into the stream.   Then when the next flood occurs these are carried down and often jam in narrow places along the channel, thereby causing fresh changes in the river.   The word "meander" is from the Latin name of the river Mæander in Phrygia, which had many windings

THE STRANGE STORY OF A PEAT BOG

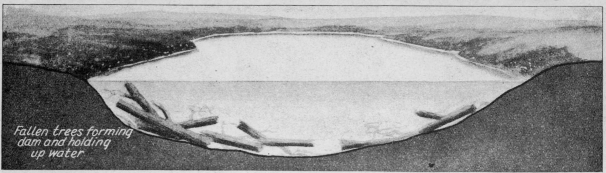

Fallen trees forming dam and holding up water

Peat bogs are found in many parts of Europe, and one-seventh of the area of Ireland consists of peat bogs. The pictures on this page show how these bogs are formed. At some time in the past an area has become covered with water, possibly owing to the damming up of a small stream by fallen trees. More and more water has accumulated, until at last a lake has been formed, as shown here

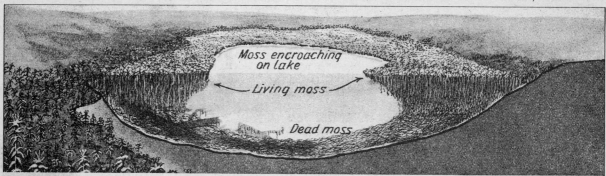

Moss encroaching on lake

Living moss

Dead moss

The wet conditions are ideal for the spread of the sphagnum or peat mosses, which always thrive in places where there is plenty of water. These mosses continue to grow and branch year after year, and gradually they spread out over the lake, while the stems below are constantly dying. Farther and farther they reach out into the lake, the vegetation increasing till the margin becomes a swamp

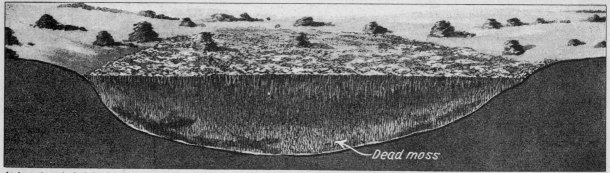

Dead moss

At last the whole lake is covered with a tangled mass, and the moss gets thicker and thicker, the dead plants and stems gradually filling up the lake till it becomes a spongy mass of vegetation, living and dead. In course of time it becomes so thick that it can be walked across, and the decaying vegetable matter, mixed with soil blown upon the bog, enables the seeds of other plants to take root

In the course of years—it may be thirty or forty, or it may be a century or two—what was once a lake has become a peat bog anything from six to forty feet deep. The peat is cut and dried, but even when dried it contains a great deal of moisture. It forms a useful fuel where coal and wood are scarce, for it contains about sixty per cent. of carbon. The antiseptic powers of peat preserve animal remains

HOW WE KNOW THAT THE GROUND SINKS AND RISES

Much of the ground on which we walk was once under the sea. This is true of most of England. As we walk over the chalk downs we are walking over myriads of tiny shells of sea creatures which, when they died, fell to the bottom of the sea, and were gradually compressed into solid chalk rock. Then later the sea-bed was upheaved. But in some places the dry land has been under the sea more than once. This is the case with some parts of Italy, and a wonderful proof of this fact is to be found in the ruins of the ancient temple of Jupiter Serapis at the little town of Pozzuoli, near Naples, shown here as it appeared in the third century

Pillars of ruined temple submerged to a height of 21 feet

Gradually the land on which the temple stood sank, till the waters of the sea encroached and submerged the temple, as shown in this picture. This was in the ninth century, and we know that the water rose till the pillars of the temple were 21 feet under water. The lower part of each column was at that time buried in the sand. How we know this is explained below

Bands where rock-boring molluscs have eaten into the stone pillars

Here we see what the temple of Jupiter Serapis looks like at the present day, and the picture explains how it is we know that the ruins have been under the sea, and how far they were submerged. On each of the standing columns at a height ranging between 12 and 21 feet there is a band showing a roughened surface. An examination of this roughened surface shows that it has been produced by the borings of a small marine mollusc called lithodomus which lives in the waters of the Bay of Naples, and some of its shells are still to be seen in the cavities on the temple columns. It is clear that what happened is that the whole of the ground was submerged to a depth at which the lithodomus could bore into the pillars, and that below the bands the pillars were buried in sand, which prevented the mollusc from working on the lower parts of the columns. Later the whole was raised out of the water again

HOW GEOLOGY MAKES THE LANDSCAPE

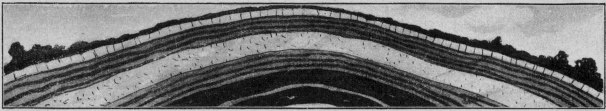

The scenery of a country is largely made by its geology, as the pictures on this page show. Here we see how the strata of rocks deposited in water through the course of ages and hardened by the pressure on top have been folded or contorted in an upward direction

The contortion or bending of the strata was caused by pressure at the sides as the Earth shrank in cooling. As time went by the wind and rain and rivers, and in some places the sea, wore away the upper rocks till the layer of strata became as shown here in section

The landscape of a region where the rocks have been folded in an upward curve, as shown above, and then worn away indicates the geological character of this part of the Earth's crust. An arched or upward curve of the strata is called by geologists an anticlinal fold

When the curve of the strata, owing to pressure at the sides, is downward, so as to form a trough instead of an arch, it is called a synclinal fold, and such we see here. The word synclinal means "inclined together," while anticlinal means "oppositely inclined"

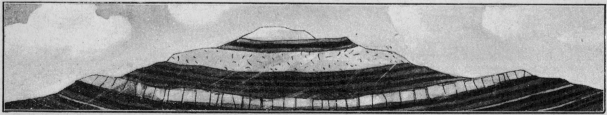

In this picture we see the previous strata in section after the weathering has gone on for ages, and rivers, rain and wind have worn away much of the upper rock. Rivers are, of course, great sculptors of the landscape, as we see in the Colorado Canyon on page 32

This picture shows the kind of landscape we get where the geological formation is a synclinal fold. Both forms of landscape are seen in scores of places in   other countries   Contorted strata over a large area show both anticlinal and synclinal folds

HOW MEN FIGHT THE ONRUSH OF THE SAND

The sand of beaches exposed to strong winds blowing from the sea is often driven inland, forming mounds and ridges known as sand dunes. Sometimes these are seventy or eighty feet high and run along the coast for miles. Unless resisted by the planting of grass they eventually bury trees, buildings, and even towns as has happened over wide areas of North Africa, Arabia and Eastern Asia

To prevent the sand blowing farther and farther inland man fights the advancing enemy with the only effective weapon he knows namely, plants that thrive on sand. Grasses like marram grass and sea couch grass grow readily and their roots and stems form a network that arrests the sand and prevents much of it from blowing farther inland

Then trees are planted and these help still further to arrest the sands, though if there are enormous quantities of sand and regular winds practically nothing can, in the long run, stay the onward march of the foe. The maritime pine, yielding resin, is a favourite tree for this purpose. The sand ridges interrupt the drainage from the interior and as the water collects marshes are formed as in the Landes region of France, where men are compelled to go about on stilts

HOW A CORAL ISLAND IS FORMED

These pictures show how a coral island is formed, according to Darwin. First of all the coral polyps, which must live in shallow water, begin building their framework round a volcanic island near the surface. Gradually the island sinks, and as the polyps die fresh frameworks are built, until there is a hard mass of rocky coral forming a fringe round the old island, just below the surface of the water, as shown here. This is known to students of geography as a Fringing Reef. Later stages in the history of the coral island are given below

As the island sinks the coral polyps go on building up the reef, which now extends a considerable distance from the land. The reef on the sea side is very steep, and between it and the island is a deep lagoon. The reef is now called a Barrier Reef

Still the old island goes on sinking, and the polyps go on building, till at last the land has disappeared altogether, and now there is nothing but a ring of coral rising out of the deep ocean with a depth of perhaps a quarter of a mile, and a lagoon inside

This is what the coral island or atoll looks like in its last stage. The reef is piled up by masses of coral being broken off and thrown up by the waves. By weathering, the surface is broken up into soil, and vegetation begins from seeds washed ashore or dropped by birds

THREE CHAPTERS IN THE HISTORY OF A LANDSLIDE

At the beginning of the present century a great landslide occurred on Turtle Mountain in Alberta, Canada, when a great mass of earth suddenly broke loose from the face of the mountain and slid into the valley below. There had been torrential rains as shown here, and the water had accumulated along the strata making it slippery. Extensive mining tunnels had weakened the mountain base

Suddenly a mass of material nearly half a square mile in area and four or five hundred feet in thickness broke loose and started travelling down faster than an express train. It slid a distance of two miles and a half in about a hundred seconds, having been set moving by a series of earthquake shocks which shook the mass of rock loose. Many lives were lost and many buildings destroyed by the catastrophe

The landslide crossed the valley half a mile wide like lightning, and rushed up the hill on the opposite side for several hundred feet, so great was the impetus which it received as it slid down the mountain-side. When it finally came to rest the mass of fallen material covered an area of more than a square mile and the whole landscape of the countryside was greatly changed in appearance

SOME WAYS IN WHICH LAKES ARE FORMED

Newland lakes

Basin range lakes

Coulee lake

Rift valley lake

Crater lake

Morainal lake

Earthquake lakes

Landslide lake

Ox-bow lakes

Saucer lake

Paternoster lakes

Delta lakes

Dune lakes

Sink lake

Playa lake

On this page we see some of the more familiar types of lake which are to be seen in different parts of the world. Different names are given to the lakes according to their method of formation, and we read of the causes which lead to these different kinds of lake appearing. Sometimes the land sinks, or is dislocated by an earthquake ; sometimes a barrier accumulates and holds up the water, and sometimes a part of a river may be cut off from the stream and become a lake. So long as the lake receives more water than is lost by evaporation it continues to exist. The Dead Sea is an example of the rift valley lake, and there are plenty of oxbow lakes in the Mississippi area. Countries like Switzerland and Norway show examples of the various glacial lakes, and in any large river delta there are delta lakes. Dune lakes are found in the Landes district of France. A playa lake is found in a dry region where the annual rainfall has diminished and the river beds run dry or almost so. Here lakes become more or less salt by evaporation, and when in-flowing streams bring much sediment a playa or mud plain is formed

THE STRANGE TALE OF A BURIED TOWN

Towns have often been buried by drifting sand. We find this in the Sahara and Gobi Deserts. But in northern Europe something even more astonishing has happened. On the south-eastern shore of the Baltic Sea there used to be a town called Kunzen, shown here

On the great barrier beach close by were sand dunes, and as the wind blew it gradually carried the sand nearer and nearer to the town, till it began to bury the houses and the church, as shown in this picture, which is the second chapter in the strange history of Kunzen

Nothing could stay the onward progress of the advancing sand dunes, and in the course of time the whole town was completely buried under the sand, as shown here. So far as any outward sign of the existence of Kunzen was concerned, it might never have been

But still the sand dunes moved on, and in the course of years had passed so far that what had once been the flourishing town of Kunzen was once more exposed to sight. In this part of the Baltic shores other villages have similarly been buried and later on unveiled again

THREE STAGES IN THE HISTORY OF THE ALPS

Sandstone

Limestone

Sandstone

Granite

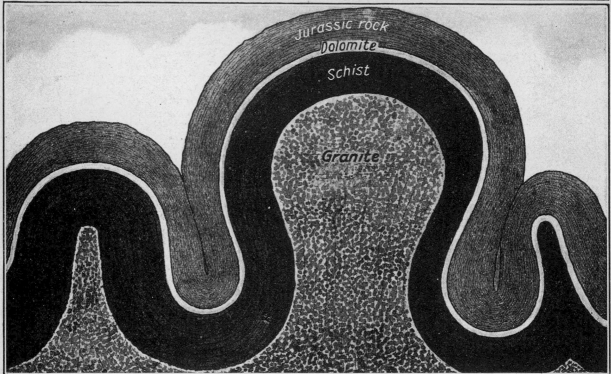

Jurassic rock

Dolomite

Schist

Granite

Jurassic rock

Dolomite

Schist

Granite

Jurassic rock

Dolomite

Schist

The Alps, which rise from 5,000 to 15,000 feet above sea level, were the terror of the ancient world, but they have now become the playground of Europe. How was this great mountain range formed? Well, the pictures on this page show three stages in its history. The Alps are made up of different kinds of rock, and originally these rocks were deposited in successive layers, as shown in the top picture. This means that at one time the Alpine region was under water. Then it was raised up out of the sea, and owing to pressure from the sides the layers of rock were folded and twisted. This stage is shown in the second picture. But all the time the wind and weather have been at work wearing away the softer rocks. Even the hard granite has been much eroded and is very uneven in shape, as we can see in the third picture which shows a section through the Mont Blanc range with Mont Blanc itself in the centre

Book 4

▼▼▼▼▼▼▼▼▼▼▼

SECRETS of
the WEATHER
SIMPLIFIED

▲▲▲▲▲▲▲▲▲▲▲

FINE WEATHER ABOVE THE RAINCLOUD

The nimbus, or rain cloud, is a dense, dark sheet of cloud without any particular form, and it may be as low as 200 feet above the ground, or it may be as high as 18,000 feet. Generally it is about three-quarters of a mile. As soon as the cloud becomes overloaded with moisture and its particles of water are too heavy to be sustained in the air, they fall as rain. But above the cloud the sun will be shining, and airmen have had the strange experience of flying beneath a blue sky in sunshine, while underneath them was the black cloud pouring down water on the city or country below. This picture shows the different weather conditions above and below the cloud.

STORMS ON THE SUN & STORMS ON THE EARTH

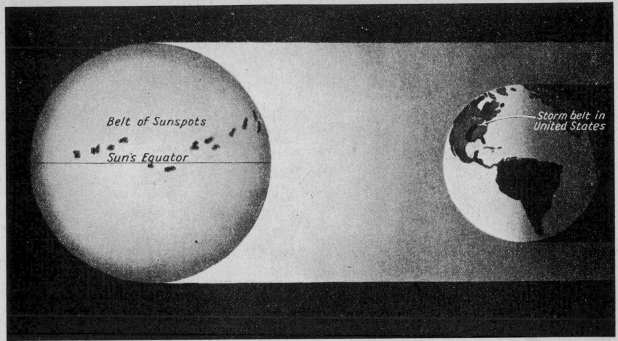

It has long been known that the spots on the Sun's face, which are really whirling storms of gigantic size, affect conditions on the Earth. The displays of the Aurora and the variations of the magnetic needle correspond almost exactly with the variations in the sunspots. But researches by meteorologists in conjunction with the discoveries of astronomers, have shown that the sunspots have some influence on the Earth's weather. We are at present only at the beginning of the study of this subject, but already it has been found that storm areas on the Earth move as the Sun's spots change their position. In this picture we see a line of sunspots on the Sun's surface and a storm belt in the United States. This particular storm belt has been specially studied in connection with the position of the sunspots

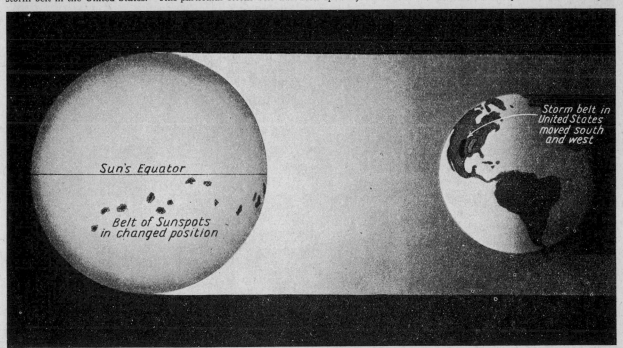

In the two pictures on this page taken together the artist has tried to convey to our eye some idea of how the sunspots affect the weather. Researches over many years have shown that when the belt of sunspots changes its latitude or position on the Sun's face, the storm area in the United States also moves its position. We see by comparing this picture with the one above that as the line of sunspots has moved, so the storm belt in North America has moved farther south and west. Records of the appearance of sunspots have been kept for nearly a century and a half, but weather records for those years are not so continuous. It will be necessary for meteorologists to watch the weather conditions for many years to come and to compare them with the sunspot cycles before they can come to definite conclusions

THE MYSTERY OF THE RAINBOW IN THE SKY

When the horizon does not get in the way a rainbow is seen as a full circle of colour. Of course, when we are standing on the Earth we can never see a rainbow in this form but the airman who goes high up above the clouds and looks down at the rainbow from above sees it in this circular form, and just as we often see from the Earth a second and fainter rainbow with the colours reversed so the airman sees a double circle of colour, as illustrated in this picture. In the centre of the rainbow he sees the shadow of his aircraft.

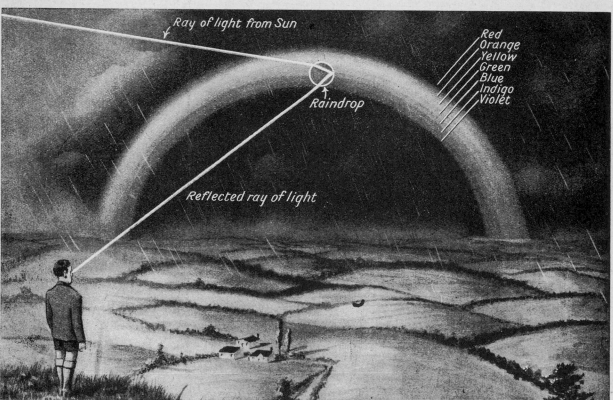

In this picture we see how a rainbow is caused. A ray of light from the Sun strikes a raindrop, is bent as it passes through it, and is then reflected back again from the inside of the drop and being bent once more reaches our eye. But the ray of light from the Sun is not only bent and reflected ; it is broken up, or refracted, as men of science say. This divides it up into the seven colours, violet, indigo, blue, green, yellow, orange, red, and it is these colours which we see. Of course, it is not only the light reflected from one raindrop which reaches our eye, but from many. We do not see all the colours from the one raindrop. The particular colour we see from each drop depends upon the angle at which the light from it is reflected to our eye. From this explanation of how the rainbow is formed it will be clear that no two people can possibly see the same rainbow, for we all have the colours reflected to our eye from different drops of rain.

HOW THE MOISTURE GETS INTO THE AIR

Further condensation due to clouds rising or coming into contact with cold air currents

Condensation due to cold layer of air

From Volcano

From Geyser

From Hot Springs

From Vegetation

From Pond

From Lake

From River

From Moist Earth

Underground water

From Sea

The bulk of the moisture which gets into the air is evaporated by the Sun from the sea. But it must be remembered that moisture does not rise only from the sea. There are many other sources of the aqueous vapour in the air, and these are shown in this picture-diagram, which is from a design by Mr. Kenneth A. Ray, M.A. Water rises from rivers, lakes, ponds, hot springs and geysers. A certain amount also gets into the air from volcanoes, for steam is thrown into the air during a volcanic eruption, especially if snow or water has accumulated in the crater during a period of rest. Then a great deal of moisture rises through the earth from underground water sources, and vegetation also gives off a great deal of moisture. All these sources shown in the picture contribute to the moisture in the air, which as it travels and strikes colder layers of air is condensed into small drops of water that form clouds ; or, if they are near the surface of the Earth, fogs. When the clouds strike still colder layers of air more water is condensed, the drops of moisture get too heavy to be suspended any longer, and fall as rain, or if the air is very cold the vapour is frozen into crystals which form snowflakes and fall as snow. So the endless round of evaporation and condensation goes on all over the world, though in some parts there is far more than in others

PLACES TO AVOID IN A THUNDERSTORM

Many people have a great feeling of terror during a thunderstorm, their fear being caused more by the harmless thunder than the lightning flash which is the real cause of danger. But while we do not want to be unduly fearful, we should be very careful to avoid positions where the lightning may possibly strike. It is always best to keep away from metal articles like railings, taps, pots and pans, and so on. Out of doors we should never stand under a tree, near a metal fence or pump, or in the centre of a bare field or other open space where we are the tallest object. It is also wise to keep away from hills and eminences. If the lightning strikes it is liable to strike the tallest object. Indoors it is best to keep in the middle of the room, away from doors and windows, and in a railway carriage away from the sides

THE STRANGE ANTICS OF A BALL OF FIRE

From time to time a strange form of lightning is seen. It appears as a ball of fire and travels slowly, constantly changing its direction. In this picture we see the course of one of these fireballs, known as globe lightning. It originated as one ball, but on touching the ground split into two. These rose and while one went down the chimney of a house and exploded, doing great damage, the other followed a more erratic course. It went down the chimney of another house, crossed a room in which were a man and a child, doing no harm to either and then, making a small hole in the floor, went through into the chamber beneath, used as a sheep-fold. The lambs started jumping about, and five older sheep were killed. The shepherd's son at the door was not injured. The ball then passed out at the doorway

RAIN FALLING OVER THE DRY DESERT

Rain clouds from the sea

Rain falling

Hot air evaporating rain as it falls

There are parts of the Sahara where the ground is perfectly dry, and is never moistened by rain from one year's end to another. Yet even in these parts from time to time clouds are seen in the sky, blown across by the winds from the sea, and these clouds, reaching cold layers of air above, yield up their moisture, which falls as rain. But where does the rain go, seeing it never reaches the parched, sandy ground below? Well, as it falls from the colder regions above it reaches layers of air made hot by radiation from the sun-warmed ground, and here the rain evaporates while falling, changing back into invisible water vapour

LAND AND SEA BREEZES AND THEIR CAUSE

Even under the calmest conditions there is always a breeze blowing at the seaside. In the daytime it blows from the sea upon the land, and at night from the land towards the sea. The pictures on this page show why the land and sea breezes blow in this way. Here in this top picture we have the conditions that make a sea breeze. During the day the land, being a solid, takes up heat from the Sun more quickly than the adjacent water, and warms the air above it, so that this rises, and the cooler air that is over the sea flows in to take its place. Thus a constant stream of cool air is passing over the land from the sea

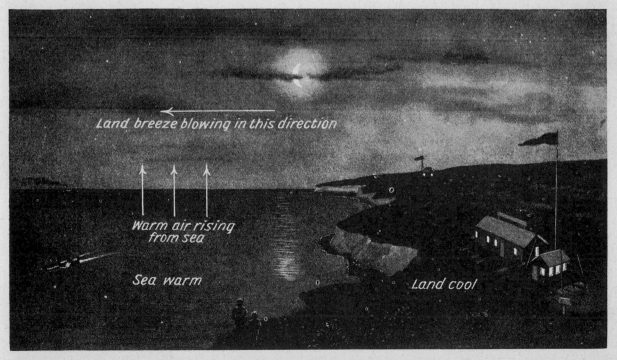

Here we see the conditions that produce a land breeze, that is, a wind blowing from the land towards the sea. At night the land that has become heated during the day gives up its heat rapidly, and becomes cool. But the sea, which was slow in taking in the Sun's heat, is also slow in giving it up. The result is that the land is cooler than the sea. Warm air over the sea therefore rises, and cool air from the land flows in to take its place. The arrows in these pictures show the direction of the air currents, not the winds themselves

HOW THE SUN WORKS NIAGARA FALLS

Every minute 167 million gallons of water crash over the limestone precipice at Niagara and fall 155 feet into the river below. As the water falls it generates many millions of horse-power, and men, realising that so much power was going to waste, have harnessed about four million horse-power to generate electric light and work machinery over hundreds of square miles. How is all this power produced at Niagara? This picture explains the matter. It is the Sun that works Niagara Falls. Its rays fall upon the ocean, warming the surface, so that evaporation is constantly going on, and the water vapour, being light, rises. The winds carry it till it reaches a cooler region where it is condensed into particles of water, forming clouds. Then, when the clouds get too heavy to float in the air, they fall as rain. The water runs into the river-bed, where it flows towards the sea, pouring over the precipice at Niagara on its way

WHY A TORNADO IS SO DESTRUCTIVE

A tornado is the most destructive of all storms, and when one passes it cuts down trees and telegraph poles and fences and houses, as though a gigantic scythe had been at work. The tornado is a spiral wind whirling round at terrific speed. It is said that sometimes the speed of this rotating wind is as much as 500 miles an hour. The great funnel of spiral wind travels across country at anything from twenty to fifty miles an hour. The diameter of the tornado is generally less than a thousand feet, and it leaves behind it a strip of devastated country of that width. As the wind whirls round it cuts down everything in its way with strange results. One side of the funnel of wind will strike a fence or a plantation and throw down everything in one direction, and then when in its rotation it strikes the fence again everything is blown down in the opposite direction. A vacuum is created in the centre of the whirling wind with the result that buildings explode outwards, the pressure of the air in the rooms forcing the walls out into the vacuum. Records for ten years show that in the United States the average annual number of tornadoes was 146. In regions where they are likely to occur the people in many cases prepare what are known as cyclone cellars, in which they take refuge during the passage of the storm

THE MANY BEAUTIFUL FORMS OF THE SNOWFLAKES

Snowflakes look very much alike as they fall, but if they are examined through a microscope they exhibit all kinds of beautiful forms, and their variety may almost be described as legion. The crystals consist of minute needles which combine to form symmetrical figures with six sides or six rays, but however they combine they always do so at angles of sixty degrees. There are literally thousands of forms which the snow crystals assume, and all those that are given on this page were taken from actual examples. This symmetrical formation in snow has been observed from ancient times. Aristotle refers to it. Of course when snow is falling heavily and the flakes press upon one another as they reach the ground the symmetrical formation is often spoilt. Their beauty is best seen during a light fall

Book 5

▼▼▼▼▼▼▼▼▼▼▼▼▼▼▼

THROUGH *the*

WONDERLAND

of NATURE

▲▲▲▲▲▲▲▲▲▲▲▲▲▲▲

Singapore
12 hours

Madras
Duration of longest day

Calcutta
13½ hours

Cairo
14 hours

Valetta
14½ hours

Rome
15 hours

The picture on these pages makes clear why it is that some places are hot and other places cold. The warmth of every place depends upon the Sun, for it is only the Sun's heat that makes the Earth a habitable world at all. But though the Sun shines upon the whole Earth there are differences of temperature due to the fact that the Sun's rays strike some places much more slantingly than others. It is because the Earth is tilted as it travels round the Sun that some parts of the Earth are very warm and some very cold. If the Earth were upright instead of tilted, the Sun's rays would strike directly upon every part of the Earth, and there would be tropical weather in all parts. The more directly overhead the Sun is the hotter are its rays, whereas the farther away we get from the Equator the more slantingly the rays strike, and the less powerful they are, till at last in the region of the Poles they are so slanting as to give

Paris
16 hours

London
16½ hours

Edinburgh
17½ hours

Leningrad
18½ hours

Trondjhem
20 hours

very little heat at all. In this picture a number of well-known cities in different latitudes are shown, and we can see how directly the Sun's rays strike a city like Singapore, and how very slantingly they strike northern cities like Leningrad, and Trondjhem in Norway. It will be seen that the rays fall much more slantingly on Madras and Calcutta than on Singapore. Very few people know that Singapore is the only big and important city that is almost on the Equator. Of course Quito, the capital of Ecuador, is also near the Equator, but, being nearly two miles above sea-level, it has a temperate climate, for the higher we go the colder it gets. Most of the other cities shown are near sea-level, and so the nearer the Equator the greater is their heat. Underneath the name of each town is given the period of daylight on the longest day of the year. The kinds of animals and vegetation that live in the different latitudes are shown

WHY THE SEA IS SALT

THE MANY DIFFERENT SUBSTANCES FOUND IN SEA-WATER

WHEN we go to the seaside and bathe we know as soon as we get a mouthful of sea-water that the sea is salt. This is quite evident to the taste, and if we think at all a number of interesting questions must arise in our minds Where did the sea get its salt? How much salt is there in the sea, and why is river-water not salt?

There is a folk-lore story which professes to explain the matter by telling how a ship on board of which there was a mill grinding out salt went down to the bottom of the ocean. All the people on board were drowned, and as there was nobody to stop the mill it has gone on ever since grinding out salt. Of course, that is a picturesque story. but we must look elsewhere for the explanation of where the sea obtained its salt.

How Rivers Bring Salt

Probably the sea has always been salt. When the oceans were first condensed out of the atmosphere of gases and vapour that enveloped the planet there were no doubt in this atmosphere salt vapours, and these would be carried down by the condensing water into the primeval ocean.

But even supposing there had been no salt in the early atmosphere, and that the original ocean had been quite fresh, the water would have become salt by now. The sun pours down upon the surface of the ocean, turning the water into invisible vapour, which rises and later becomes condensed in the clouds, and then falls as rain to feed the streams and rivers. As the rivers pass over the land they dissolve a certain amount of the minerals of the Earth and carry this down with them to the sea. Then when the sun evaporates some of this water the mineral matter is left behind, dissolved in the water which remains, and so the ocean is ever getting salter.

At the present time the ocean contains on an average nearly 3½ per cent. of dissolved mineral matter. This means that in every hundred pounds of sea-water there are nearly 3½ pounds of salt.

But the salt is not all common salt, or sodium chloride, as chemists call it. That makes up a little more than three quarters of the total mineral matter dissolved in the sea, and the remainder consists of small quantities of various other salts. An analysis of the mineral matter in sea-water shows the following proportions in every 100 parts by weight: sodium chloride, or common salt, 77·76; magnesium chloride 10·88; magnesium sulphate or Epsom-salt, 4 74; calcium sulphate

or gypsum, 3·60; potassium sulphate 2·46; calcium carbonate or limestone, 0·34; and magnesium bromide, 0·22.

The popular idea that the water of rivers and lakes is fresh is quite incorrect. No such thing as pure liquid water is found anywhere in Nature; rain-water is often nearly pure, but in falling from the clouds it dissolves various gases in the atmosphere and then when it flows through the earth or over the earth it is dissolving mineral matter all the time, the gases which it has taken up from the atmosphere

A man is able to float easily in the Dead Sea of Palestine, where the density of the water is so great that it is impossible for a person to sink or drown

assisting in the work of solution River-water, therefore, is salt, but nothing like so salt as the sea, and so we cannot detect the saltness by taste As a matter of fact, the water of the ocean contains nearly 200 times as much dissolved mineral matter as the water of the rivers.

The very careful analyses of salt water which are made nowadays have shown that in addition to the substances already mentioned nearly every known element is found in solution in the sea. but most of them are in such very minute quantities that they can be detected only by the most delicate means

Watching the Crystals Form

We can see the salt in sea-water for ourselves if we carry out a simple experiment. Let us take a little sea-water and place it in a shallow vessel in a sheltered place, covering it with a sheet of paper so that no dust may get in. After a time the water will evaporate We can then put a little more sea-water in, and let that also evaporate, and by this time we shall see that a number of minute crystals have been left behind in the bottom of the vessel These crystals are the salts of the sea.

The experiment can be .made even

more interesting if, when the water has nearly evaporated, we examine a little of it through the microscope. When the water has nearly gone we stir it up and then put a drop or two on a thin glass slide under the microscope, and watch it. The water continues to go off as vapour, and as it does so we shall see the various salts forming into little bodies of definite shape, known as crystals. They seem to rush about, some of them uniting. Certain of the crystals will be oblong and pointed, and these are sulphate of lime or gypsum Others consist of tiny squares, and these are the crystals of common salt. The different shapes of the crystals indicate the different kinds of salt which were in the drop of sea-water. We read about the wonder of crystals in another part of this book

If while the crystals are on the slide under the microscope we breathe gently on it, we shall find that the moisture of our breath dissolves the crystals until at last they all disappear into a little drop of water formed from our breath

Salt Water and Fresh

The total quantity of salt in the ocean is enormous, and Dr. H. R Mill tells us that it would suffice to form a solid crust 170 feet thick over the entire surface of the sea. This volume of mineral matter would equal in size about one-fifth of all the land that now shows above the sea.

Of course, the saltness of the sea makes sea-water denser or heavier than fresh water. A bottle filled with sea-water will weigh more than the same bottle filled with river-water. If we reckon the density of perfectly pure water as 1, then the average density of sea-water is 1·026, or in other words, if a certain quantity of distilled water weighs 1,000 ounces, the same quantity of sea-water will weigh 1,026 ounces.

But all the water of the sea is not equally salt. Generally the surface water is salter than that lying below, and among the causes which operate to make the sea less or more salt are the amount of evaporation, the rainfall, and the quantity of fresh water poured into the ocean from rivers In those seas which are situated in regions where there is a great rainfall, or where large rivers like the Amazon are continually pouring in hundreds of thousands of gallons of fresh water, or as in the Arctic and Antarctic regions, melting ice adds to the quantity of fresh water, the saltness is considerably less than in those parts of the world where there is little rainfall and where the hot sun causes great evaporation

HOW THE SALTNESS OF THE SEA VARIES

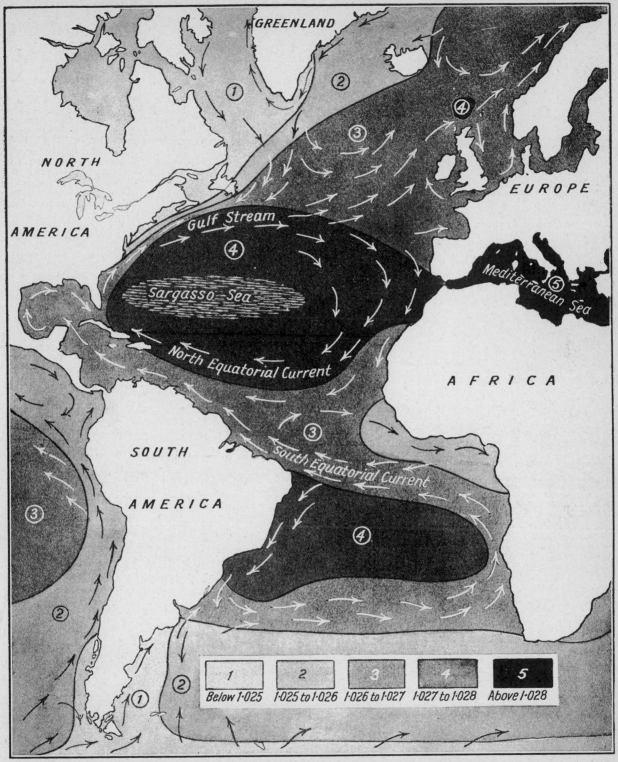

The sea is salt, but it is not equally salt in all parts. There is a considerable variation, and in this picture map of the Atlantic Ocean we see the many variations of saltness in that ocean from north to south. The percentage of salt in the sea is indicated here by the different tones, and a key to this percentage is given at the bottom. It will be noticed that the sea is less salt in the north and south, where melting icebergs add large quantities of fresh water to the sea. It is most salt where the sea is enclosed or is free from currents, as in the Mediterranean. The saltest parts are where there is most evaporation. The arrows show the course of the main currents

WHY THE SKY IS RED AT SUNSET

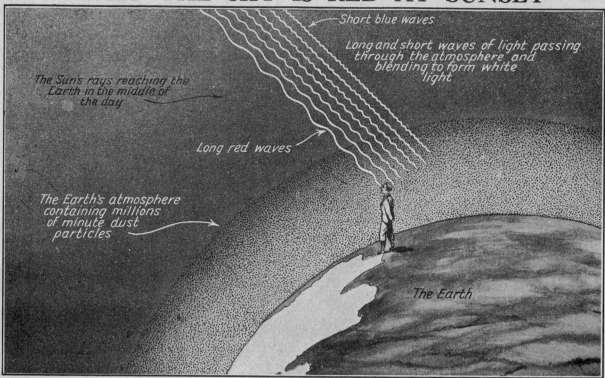

The Sun's light comes to us in rays of varying wave-lengths. As we know, sunlight is made up of seven colours, violet, indigo, blue, green, yellow, orange, red. The waves of red light are much longer than those at the other end of the spectrum, and when the rays reach our atmosphere, which is filled with myriads of tiny dust particles, the red rays with their long waves are less interfered with than the shorter blue rays. They therefore get through the atmosphere more easily. When the Sun is fairly overhead in the middle of the day there is less atmosphere to pass through, and so most of the rays get through, and mingle to make up white light

When the Sun is near the horizon at sunset the rays have to pass through a much greater thickness of atmosphere, as can be seen here. The result is that while the long waves of the red light get through to our eyes, the shorter blue rays are intercepted by the many dust particles and are reflected in all directions. When therefore we look towards the horizon the sky and clouds appear red. But if we look straight up overhead the sky will appear blue, because from that direction we receive the short blue waves reflected down from the dust particles. It is interesting on any fine summer evening to notice these two prevailing colours of the sky

THE HOTTEST AND COLDEST PLACES IN THE WORLD

We might naturally suppose that the hottest place in the world was on or near the Equator, and the coldest place round about the North and South Poles. If we thought this, however, we should be quite wrong. The temperature of a place depends on a number of different factors—whether land or water predominates in the district; whether the atmosphere is dry or moist; whether there is much wind and the direction from which this comes; the nature of the soil on which the Sun shines, and so on.

Even when the Sun is shining with the same strength it may be much

is not the hottest part of the year, for the Summer heat has not yet completely overcome the effects of the preceding Winter. As has been truly said, " The time of greatest heat lags behind the time of greatest heating."

Where then is the hottest place in the world, that is the place at which the thermometer has given the highest reading ? Well, it is nowhere near the Equator. The highest reading of the thermometer properly authenticated is 134 degrees Fah. in the shade, which was recorded in the Death Valley of Southern California. So far from being on or near the Equator, this place is

It is reported that a shade temperature of 154 degrees Fah. was read in the Sahara Desert, but this is not properly authenticated like the other.

Now where is the coldest place in the world ? Here again it is nowhere near the North or South Pole. It is a small town in Siberia, about 400 miles northeast of Yakutsk, and is near Verkhoyansk. Here in mid-Winter a temperature of rather more than 90 degrees below zero Fah. has been recorded, that is 122 degrees of frost. Yet this place is only in latitude 67 degrees, on a level with Norway and Sweden, and only just within the Arctic circle. It is

Here the same amount of sunshine is pouring upon the same place on March 21st and September 22nd, yet it is hotter in September than in March, because through the summer the soil has been taking in heat and gives off some of its accumulated warmth

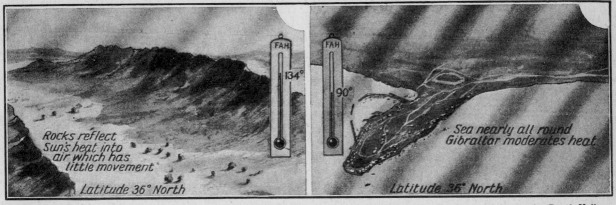

The Death Valley, California, shown on the left, and Gibraltar, shown on the right, are both at the same latitude, yet the Death Valley, because of its landlocked situation, is half as hot again as Gibraltar which is almost completely surrounded by sea

hotter at the same place on one day than it is on another. For example, it is generally much colder on March 21st, even with the same amount of sunshine, as it is on September 22nd, for on the latter day the soil, the surface rocks, if there are any, the lakes and so on, have all been warmed by the Summer, and as they cool slowly they retain and give off much of this accumulated warmth in September. On the other hand, as March 21st follows the Winter, there are no such reserves of heat.

Similarly when the Sun is at his highest in the Northern Hemisphere, it

north of the 36th degree of latitude, and is on a level with Gibraltar, whose temperature is quite moderate. The reason for the difference is that the Death Valley is a very dry area with little stirring of the air, and masses of rock exposed to the sunshine reflect the hot rays into the atmosphere and heat it to this astonishing degree.

Gibraltar, on the other hand, has water all round it, except on one side, and a place near the sea always has a cooler and more equable climate and temperature than one situated like the Death Valley.

nowhere near the sea, and not only is it remarkable for its extreme cold in Winter, but it is also remarkable for the enormous range in temperature between Summer and Winter. Though the thermometer records at times 122 degrees of frost in Winter, in Summer it rises as high as 93 degrees in the shade, a temperature we very rarely reach in London in the hottest summer.

The low temperature at Verkhoyansk in Winter is properly authenticated.

HOW THE TIDES OF THE SEA ARE CAUSED

WE are all interested in the tides. When we go to the seaside for a holiday one of the first things we do is to find out the time of high tide and low tide, and we notice great differences on the beach when the tide is in, and when it is out.

Often when the tide is out the sands are uncovered for a mile or more, and the sea seems very far away, while at high tide there are sometimes no sands to be seen, for they are quite covered by the water which reaches right up to the rocky cliffs.

What is it that causes the tides? Well, they are caused chiefly by the Moon. It was suspected two thousand years ago that the Moon had something to do with the matter, but not until Sir Isaac Newton's time were the tides fully understood.

Gravitation is the attraction which one body has for another, and just as the Sun attracts the Earth, so the Earth attracts the Moon and the Moon attracts the Earth.

being fluid, are drawn up into a bulge, and where that happens there is high tide.

Even the solid Earth yields a little to the Moon's attraction and has very small tides. The waters on the opposite side of the Earth are more distant from the Moon than the centre of the globe, and so they are not attracted as much as the solid earth, with the result that they also become bunched up into a high tide. They are, as it were, left behind when the solid Earth is pulled towards the Moon.

what it gains by size it loses by distance. It is 26,648,000 times as great in mass as the Moon, but it is 389 times as far away, so that, taking both facts into consideration, it should pull the Earth with 175 times the force that the Moon has. And this it actually does.

Why, then, are the tides caused by the Sun less than those caused by the Moon? The explanation is that the tides are due not merely to the pull itself, but to the difference between the pull on the centre of the Earth and the pull on the sides nearest and farthest from the Sun or Moon.

Now as the Earth's diameter is 8,000 miles the sides of our globe nearest to and farthest from Sun or Moon are 4,000 miles nearer or farther than the Earth's centre. This figure is a much greater proportion of 240,000 miles, the Moon's distance, than of 93,000,000 miles, the Sun's distance, and so the difference of the Moon's pull on the different parts of the Earth is much more noticeable than the difference of

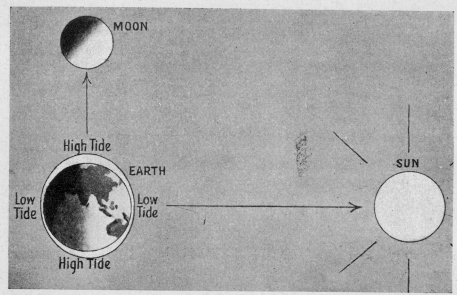

When the Sun and Moon are in this position relative to the Earth—that is, when the Moon is in its first quarter—we have what are known as neap tides. At these the sea does not rise so high as at the spring tides, explained below, for the Sun and Moon are pulling the waters of the Earth's seas in different directions, and so the two pulls to some extent counteract one another. The same thing happens when the Moon is in its third quarter

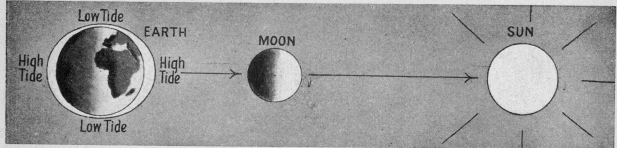

When the Sun and Moon are pulling in the same line—that is, at new Moon, as shown here, and at full Moon when the Moon is on the other side of the Earth—the double pull draws up the waters of the sea unusually high, and there are higher tides than at the neap tide position shown in the upper picture when Sun and Moon are pulling at right angles to one another. These high tides are called spring tides

This attraction shows itself as a pull. The Earth pulls the Moon and the Moon pulls the Earth.

Now, owing to this "pull of gravitation," the Moon, as it travels round the Earth, pulls the part nearest to it more than it does the centre or the other side of the Earth. This pull does not have much effect on the solid part of the Earth, but the waters of the sea,

But the Sun also pulls the Earth and draws up the waters opposite to it. If there were no Moon we should still have tides caused by the Sun's attraction. Now the Sun, being so much bigger, should pull the waters up much more than the Moon. Yet it does not do so. Why is this?

Well, in the first place the Sun is so much farther away that much of

the Sun's pull on the various parts.

When Sun and Moon pull together, as shown in the lower picture on this page, the tides are higher than when they pull against one another, as in the upper picture.

Of course, the time and the height of the tide vary in different places according to the nature of the region. The shape of the coast affects the tides.

THE GREATEST MOUNTAIN RANGE IN THE WORLD

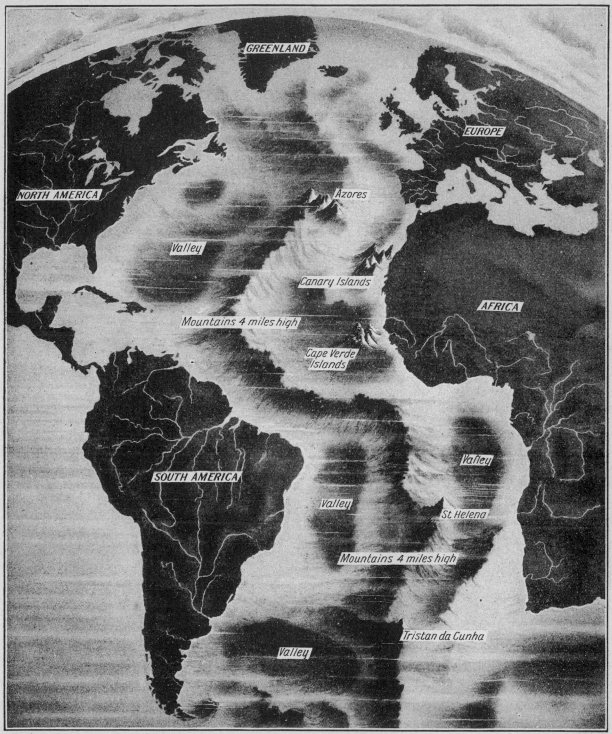

Which is the world's greatest mountain range? Many people would say the Himalayas, because of the enormous height of many of the peaks. Others might answer the Andes, because of their great length. But the greatest mountain range in the world is neither of these. It lies where no human eye has ever seen it, except for one or two of its highest peaks. It is buried beneath the Atlantic Ocean, and runs from Iceland in the north to the borders of Antarctica in the south. Rising from the lowest plains of the ocean bed, it towers up in some places to a height of nearly four miles, and in a few places the lofty peaks rise above the surface of the ocean, as at the Azores, the Cape Verde Islands, Ascension, St. Helena and Tristan da Cunha. This mighty range is ten times as long as the Himalayan chain, and is known to geographers as the Mid-Atlantic Rise. Some people have tried to identify it with the lost continent of Atlantis, of whose fame and terrible, if legendary, fate we read in the classics

THE DIFFERENT REGIONS OF THE ATMOSPHERE

Up to 450 miles. Streamers of Aurora reach here

100 to 120 miles. Second heaviside layer which bends beam wireless waves

40 to 50 miles. First heaviside layer. Ordinary wireless waves are bent here to travel round the Earth.

22 miles. Sounding balloon without instruments

20 miles. Average meteor is seen

12 miles. Sounding balloon with instruments

9 miles. Cirrus clouds

Mt Everest

It is only in recent years that men have been able to make discoveries in the upper atmosphere, which is called the stratosphere to distinguish it from the troposphere or lower part lying at a height of not more than six miles. Sounding balloons have been sent up, some with instruments and some without. From these and other sources we have learnt much. We now know that there are two distinct layers of minute nitrogen crystals known as the Heaviside layers and that these reflect the wireless waves to the Earth and prevent them being dissipated in Space. We also know where the meteorites become visible, and where the auroral displays occur

THE REGIONS OF FROST AND FIRE

LOFTY MOUNTAINS WHERE SNOW & HEAT EXIST TOGETHER

ONE of the strangest contradictions in the whole of the world of Nature is the fact that frost and fire, snow and molten rock, should be closely linked together. Yet such we find in the case of many of the three hundred volcanoes or more that are scattered about the Earth's crust and form safety valves for the molten material beneath the solid exterior.

The peaks of some of these volcanoes found in northern latitudes and along the lofty range of the Andes are perpetually snow-clad. Yet from time to time they belch out fire and molten rock.

We might well ask how it is that a mountain which is a vent for white-hot rock and has fire beneath it can be cold enough for snow to rest upon its slopes.

Well, it is true that the lava streams out at a white heat, either over the edge of the crater, or, as more often happens, through fissures in the sides of the cone. It is very hot when it first comes out, and flows rapidly, but soon it begins to cool, and it is not long before a solid crust forms over the molten stream which moves more and more slowly as it travels farther from the vent of origin.

The Lava Crust

The crust of a lava stream is a poor conductor of heat, and because of that the outside may be quite cool while underneath, and not very far down, the rock is still molten.

This fact that the solidified lava is a bad conductor of heat acts in two ways. In the first place it makes the outside of the crust cool, and it further has the effect of preventing the heat of the molten rock below from escaping through the crust into the air.

This naturally results in the molten rock retaining its heat much longer than it would otherwise do, and so it continues to flow, and often bursts through the cool crust that is rapidly forming in the front of the lava stream.

That lava when cool is a bad conductor of heat results in the slopes of an active crater being often quite cold, and when snow falls it remains frozen in its strange position. Yet the fire may not be very far off, and anyone who climbs to the top of the crater and looks over may see the molten rock below

The World's Highest Volcano

Cotopaxi, which rises in the Andes of Ecuador to a height of 19,613 feet, or nearly four miles above the level of the sea, is the highest active volcano in the world, and it is perpetually snow-covered. Yet over the crater, which is half a mile in diameter, a fiery glow is visible at night. In eruption vast quantities of hot ashes are thrown out through the mouth of this volcano, and the heat of these, by melting the snow on the slopes of the cone, causes very destructive floods which sweep into the valleys below.

It is not, however, only the loftiest volcanoes that have snow on their slopes. Even Etna, which is less than 11,000 feet high, is under snow during a large part of the year.

Formerly, of course, the Earth was much more subject to volcanic action than it is now. It is not often that we get a huge eruption, but in past ages there must have been eruptions compared with which the most severe we have experienced during the last few hundred years are mere child's play.

In the states of Idaho, Washington, and Oregon there is an area of 200,000 square miles known as the Columbia Plateau, which is formed of a series of lava sheets. In some places the lava is nearly a mile thick, and we can have only a faint idea of the eruption that could pour out such vast masses of molten rock.

Volcanoes have done a great deal of harm from man's point of view by destroying life, human, animal and plant. Large areas of once fertile country have been devastated and turned into rocky wildernesses. Yet the work of volcanoes has not been altogether without use. The burial of organic remains by streams of lava has preserved many fossils that throw light on the past history of life on the globe. Even such a destructive eruption as that of Vesuvius, which buried the cities of Pompeii and Herculaneum, preserved a record of Roman life without which we should have known much less than we do about it.

Volcanic Soil

The lava and ash poured out by volcanoes, after being weathered, make one of the richest soils in the world. The dust and ashes, when consolidated, form a soft stone known as tuff, which hardens in the air and provides an excellent building material. Some of the oldest sewers in Rome, which were built of tuff 2,500 years ago, are still in excellent condition.

Some time ago a Scottish firm purchased the cone of Vulcano, a small Mediterranean volcano, in order to get from it alum, boracic acid and sulphur, all of which are products of these fiery mountains.

Mount Etna, the Sicilian volcano, with snow on its cone not far removed from the fire and molten rock of its interior

WHY WE HAVE TO PLOUGH THE LAND

THE soil is the layer of mould which lies at the surface of our Earth's crust, and it is really the most important part of the Earth, for men, beasts, birds, insects and plants are alike dependent for their very life on what the soil produces.

The soil rests upon the harder part of the Earth's crust, which is known as the sub-soil, and if, in some great cataclysm, the whole of the soil of the Earth should be washed away we should most of us, if not all of us, perish of hunger. In some countries men have cut down forests, with the result that when the rains came they have washed the soil down the sloping hills till these became bare and hard, and nothing would grow.

The Beginning

Men of science believe that in far distant days the surface of the Earth was hard rock, but wind, and weather, and sun, and rain broke up the surface of this hard rock into powder, and thus formed a soil on which lowly plants could grow. Then the roots of these plants and various substances that resulted when they decayed broke up the rock still more and gradually a soil was formed on which more important plants could take root and from which they could draw nourishment.

If the soil is left to itself the crops of useful plants are poor. Man finds it necessary to till the soil, that is to prepare it by ploughing and in other ways, so that is shall bring forth more and more food for the use of himself and his cattle. In the old days the soil was not tilled very well, with the result that the crops were poor and the mass of people rarely knew what it was to have enough to eat. This was the case in the bleaker lands, at any rate. The more carefully the soil is prepared the more will it produce for the use of man and beast.

If the soil is left to itself it becomes hard and the roots of plants find it difficult to make their way in the earth as they seek moisture and nourishment. That is why the land has to be ploughed at regular intervals so as to break up the ground and allow the air and rain

Ploughing the soil so that the sunshine and air and rain can reach down into the earth and the ground may be broken up for the roots of plants to make their way about in it

to get in and supply fresh nourishment. It is of great importance that the soil should be gradually deepened, so that the roots of plants may find it easier to travel in search of moisture and food.

This gradual deepening of the soil is done by ploughing.

The plough cuts a furrow and turns over the soil, so that the air can get to it. Then the harrow breaks up the clods into smaller pieces and the roller crushes them still smaller. In this way the air is able to circulate freely, doing its good work in the earth.

If air is necessary to a fertile soil, so also is water. The soil must be able to hold enough moisture to carry the plant through hot, dry spells of weather, for the plant gets all its water through its roots, which are embedded in the soil. These spread about in all directions, and go deep down in search of water, and the more we help them in their search by preparing the soil the more they will help us by producing strong, healthy plants above ground. They obtain their food for the building of new tissue from the soil. There is a constant stream of water travelling through the plant, going up through the roots of the stem and passing out into the atmosphere through pores in the leaves.

A Safeguard

We know how in hot, dry summers, when there is not much rain and the soil is very dry, the leaves shrivel up. This is a provision of nature which enables the plant to retain any moisture it may have, instead of letting it pass off freely as in normal times into the air. The farmer keeps his soil in a suitable condition for holding a supply of water for use in dry and hot weather, by deep ploughing and good tilling.

Of course, the earthworms, as we read in another part of this book, do a great deal of work in preparing the soil, and make it suitable as a place in which the plants can grow, and from which they can draw nourishment. Charles Darwin made a life study of the earthworm.

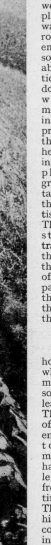

THE INSIDE OF AN ACTIVE VOLCANO

Falling ashes building up sides of volcano

Crater

Pipe of volcano

Successive layers of hardened lava

Water bubbles in lava

Fissures through which molten lava flows

Rocks formed by fire

Supply basin of lava

Drawn by L.G.Goodwin

The Earth on which we live has a very hot interior.   It was once a ball of fire, but the outside has cooled down into a hard crust, though underneath rocks are still in a molten state.   From time to time there are underground explosions, and it is fortunate for us who live on the outside of the crust that the Earth has all round it a number of safety valves where the hot gases can escape, otherwise great areas of the Earth's crust might be blown away.   These safety valves we call volcanoes, and here we see the inside of a volcano, with its reservoir of molten rock, or lava.   We are not sure what causes the periodic explosions underground, though we know that in many cases they are due to sea water trickling through cracks in the Earth's crust and reaching a bed of molten rock, when it is instantly turned into steam and hurls up masses of lava with ashes, hot gases and steam.   The conical mountain that we call a volcano is really only part of it, as we see above.   The volcano includes those parts that are out of sight, deep down in the Earth's crust

HOW THE SEA VARIES IN TEMPERATURE

ANYONE who bathes knows how very much the sea varies in temperature. Even in the course of a day or two it may change a great deal, and in different parts of the world the variations are far greater. In the Arctic and Antarctic the water is almost at freezing point, while in the upper part of the Red Sea it is about 90 degrees.

Speaking generally, it is the strength of the Sun's rays that makes the water warm or cold. These rays do not penetrate into the sea to a greater depth than about 600 feet, and the consequence is that the deep water, which is the greater part of the entire ocean, has a much more regular temperature at any given spot throughout the year than the surface water.

At the surface the water changes according to the season, and it is also greatly affected by currents. Naturally the surface of the ocean, like that of the land, is warmer near the Equator

Equator to the Poles. Many rivers enter the sea and these often in summer bring water that is warmer than the sea-water, while in winter their water is sometimes colder than the sea.

The surface of the sea is always cooler at night than during the day, and it is cooler in winter than in summer. These changes from day to day and from season to season are much less than those of the land in the same latitude.

When, however, we come to go deeper than the surface we find that the water becomes cooler with increasing depth. There is an exception, however, where the surface water is nearly freezing.

Even where the surface water is warmest, as in the equatorial regions, the temperature, directly we go a few hundred fathoms down, gets very low. On an average when we go 600 feet below the surface the temperature is just over 60 degrees Fahrenheit; at twice that depth, namely, 1,200 feet, it

sea, where the temperature falls from about 75 degrees at the surface to 55 degrees at a depth of 750 feet, and then remains unchanged to the bottom, which is 13,000 feet below the surface. At this depth the temperature of the ocean outside is 37 degrees Fahrenheit.

What is the reason that these enclosed seas show such a high temperature deep down? Well, the reason is that there are sunken barriers of rock which shut them off more or less from the open ocean. The result is that the colder and denser water outside is prevented from flowing in and displacing the warmer and lighter waters that lie below the top of the barrier. The picture-diagram on this page illustrates this point.

As a matter of fact, the temperature of the bottom of these enclosed seas is often about the same as the temperature of the sea-water at the level of the top of the barrier, which separates them from the ocean.

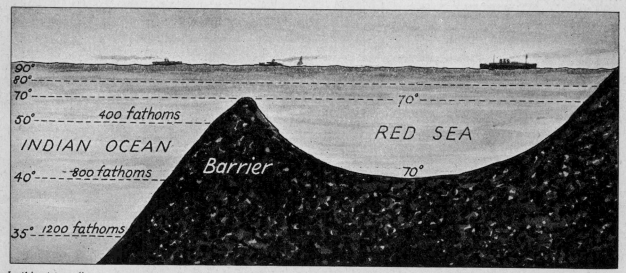

In this picture-diagram we see a section through the Red Sea and the part of the Indian Ocean which joins it. The temperature of the surface water is the same in both seas, but as can be seen, a great rocky barrier shuts off the deeper part of the Indian Ocean from the Red Sea, and prevents the colder water of the Ocean's lower depths from flowing in. The result is that the temperature of the Red Sea below the surface remains the same as it is at the top of the barrier, namely, 70 degrees Fahrenheit

and gets cooler towards the Poles. Near the Equator the temperature of the surface water is generally about 80 degrees Fahrenheit, while near the Poles it is about 28 degrees Fahrenheit. That, of course, is below the freezing point of fresh water, which is 32 degrees Fahrenheit, but it takes greater cold to freeze salt water than fresh water.

The temperature of the surface water depends a great deal upon the currents. Some of these are cold and flow into warmer water, lowering the temperature. The Labrador current is a good example of this. On the other hand, a warm current often flows into cooler water raising the temperature, and the Gulf Stream is a striking example of this.

But there are other reasons why the surface water of the ocean does not get colder steadily as we travel from the

is 50 degrees; at 3,000 feet it is about 40 degrees; at 6,000 it is 36½ degrees.

Men of science who have studied the sea tell us that not more than one-fifth of the water of the ocean has a temperature as high as 40 degrees Fahrenheit. The average temperature of the whole of the sea is reckoned to be about 39 degrees Fahrenheit. At the bottom of the deeper parts the temperature is below 35 degrees.

These facts, however, do not apply to the deeper parts of enclosed seas. For instance, the Red Sea, which is about 3,600 feet deep, often has a temperature of 90 degrees Fahrenheit at the surface. This is reduced to 70 degrees at a depth of 1,200 feet, and it remains about the same to the very bottom.

A similar state of things is found in the Mediterranean, another enclosed

The great mass of deep sea-water is cold because cold water at the surface always tends to sink owing to its greater density, and as the supply of icy water from the polar regions is very great, there is a constant supply of cold water to go on sinking. When the ice caps melt the cold water is fresh, and therefore lighter than sea-water, but it soon gets mixed with the salt water and then becomes heavy enough to sink.

It might be asked how men discover the temperature of the water deep down in the ocean. Well, they have two methods. One is to let down specially constructed thermometers which register the temperature, while another is to lower special bottles which bring up specimens of the deep water.

THE WAY IN WHICH THE DEW IS FORMED

Dew, as everybody knows, consists of small drops of water which gather on leaves, the blades of grass, the threads of spiders' webs, and indeed on most objects that are out in the open at night. The drops are condensed from water vapour, but up to recent times it has not been known definitely how the dew was formed, that is, the source of the vapour from which the dewdrops condensed.

The experiments carried out by a Cambridge scientist were very interesting, and are shown in picture form on this page. First of all he inverted a tin over certain blades of grass, letting the tin into the ground to shield these blades from the atmosphere. In the morning he found that the grass all round the tin was covered with drops of dew, but when he raised the tin the grass underneath had no dew whatever

blades, but lowered it into the ground, replacing the turf in the tin. The next morning when he examined the place he found that the grass all round the tin was covered with dewdrops, while that in the tin had no dew whatever.

On this occasion the moisture had risen from the ground and had been precipitated as drops of water on the blades of grass. But where the moisture could not rise because of the interven-

In the left-hand picture the tin, shown in section, was inverted over the grass as evening fell, and the next morning dew was found on the grass all round, as shown on the right, but when the tin was removed there was no dew on the grass under the tin. This showed that the dew was precipitated from the air and the grass under the tin was dry because the moist air could not get to it

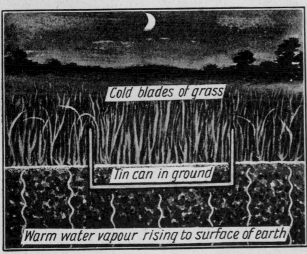

In this experiment the tin was let into the ground, the grass being replaced in the tin as shown on the left. The next morning there was dew on the grass all round, but no dew on the grass that had the tin under it. In this case it was clear that the dew was not precipitated from the air, but was caused by moisture rising from the soil. No moisture could rise where the tin acted as a barrier

Poets used to write about the dew "falling," but dew does not fall like rain. The vapour all round the grass and leaves suddenly becomes chilled, and, as a result, condenses into drops of water. It was supposed for a long time that all this moisture came from the atmosphere, but recent experiments have shown that this is not the case.

upon it. It was clear therefore that in this case the dew had been derived from the moisture in the atmosphere, that it had not "risen from the ground," as many people suppose the dew always does.

On another night the scientist carried out a second experiment. This time he did not invert the tin over the grass

tion of the tin the grass thus protected had no dew whatever.

The experiments described read remarkably like the story in the Book of Judges, of Gideon and the fleece which he laid out at night. On one night the fleece was covered with dew but not the surrounding ground, while on the next night the ground was dewy but not the fleece.

Volume II

WONDERS
OF
POPULAR
SCIENCE

Contents—Volume II. Wonders of Popular Science

BOOK 6. PICTORIAL OUTLINE OF PROGRESS

BOOK 7. AMAZING ADVENTURES IN SCIENCE

BOOK 8. THE SEVEN WONDERS OF THE MODERN WORLD

BOOK 9. MANUAL OF SIMPLIFIED EXPERIMENTS

BOOK 10. BEHIND THE SCENES OF GREAT INVENTIONS

Book 6

PICTORIAL OUTLINE of PROGRESS

MAN LEARNS HOW TO TALK ACROSS SPACE

To talk across space has always been the ambition of mankind from the very earliest times, when the Stone Age man sent a message across a river or valley by waving his arms or lighting a fire, so that its smoke could be seen by day and its glare by night. Beacon fires were used right through the centuries, and we know how news of the coming of the Spanish Armada was flashed across England by means of beacons. Not, however, till modern times was any really scientific method of communicating at a distance attempted. In 1767 the father of Maria Edgeworth, the novelist, experimented in sending messages across country by moving windmill sails. Then he invented four triangular signs and a code, the positions of the triangles representing the numbers in the code. Later a Venetian blind arrangement was invented in France, and improved into a framework of shutters in England Next came the semaphore, by which news could be sent from London to Portsmouth in a few minutes. Signalling discs were also used by soldiers, and later came the heliograph, and in 1837 the electric telegraph. In 1877 Dr. Bell invented the telephone. and last of all came wireless

PENS AND WRITING THROUGH THE AGES

Cave man's picture writing

Egyptian chiselling hieroglyphics on wall

Babylonian inscribing cuneiform writing on clay tablet

Scratching hieroglyphics on pottery fragment

Oriental with inkhorn

Monk writing on parchment with reed pen

Roman writing with stylus on wax tablet

IVLIVS

Writing on papyrus

Quill pen

Typewriter

Slate and pencil

Blacklead pencil

Writing with steel pen nib

Fountain pen

In these pictures we see the different ways in which man has written from the early times when the Stone Age man recorded incidents in pictures on his cave walls, and on the bones of animals. The early Egyptian writing known as hieroglyphics consisted of pictures which were later modified into simpler signs. These writings were chiselled on stone walls or scratched on fragments of pottery, but later the Egyptians wrote with ink on papyrus, a reed that grew by the banks of the Nile. The Babylonians and Assyrians wrote in cuneiform or wedge-shaped characters on clay tablets and cylinders, impressing the signs by means of a wedge-shaped tool. The Greeks and Romans also wrote on papyrus, and sometimes on parchment, but the Romans wrote their personal letters on wax tablets, impressing the letters with a pointed implement called a stylus. The other end of the stylus was flat, so that if they made a mistake in the writing they could press the wax smooth and write the letter again. In the Middle Ages parchment was employed for writing, a reed pen being used, and the ink kept in a receptacle called an inkhorn, originally made of horn, but later of brass. This type of inkhorn is still used in the East. Later came the quill pen the writing being dried by means of fine sand sprinkled from a sand box, like a pepper-pot. The blacklead pencil, the slate and pencil and the steel pen nib were all later inventions, and then came the fountain pen, and the typewriter

HOW THE HOUSE HAS DEVELOPED FROM THE CAVE

CAVE DWELLING

TREE SHELTER

SKIN SHELTER

LAKE DWELLING

ROUND STONE HOUSE

EGYPTIAN BRICK HOUSE

ASSYRIAN HOUSE

PHŒNICIAN HOUSE

MEDIEVAL STONE HOUSE

ROMAN VILLA

HALF-TIMBERED HOUSE

GEORGIAN HOUSE

MODERN VILLA

On this page we see how the home of man has developed from a natural cave in which he took shelter from the weather to the house of to-day with its comforts and labour-saving conveniences. Man needs a shelter no matter in what land he lives, for if he is in a hot country he wants protection from the Sun, and if he is in a cold land he must take shelter from the weather. A cave was the natural shelter for primitive man, but as the fierce animals often wanted to share it with him, he found it convenient to build some kind of a home in a tree. Then he dug a pit and covered it with branches and turf, and later built a house of wood or stone or skin, according to the material most easily available. Slowly the house was improved, and the Ancient Egyptians, the Greeks, the Romans and other peoples built very fine houses. The Romans, for example, introduced central heating. The   house has been developed in many pic-turesque styles, but only in recent times have ventilation and sanitation been regarded as important items in the planning of a house

THE EVOLUTION OF HOUSE-WARMING

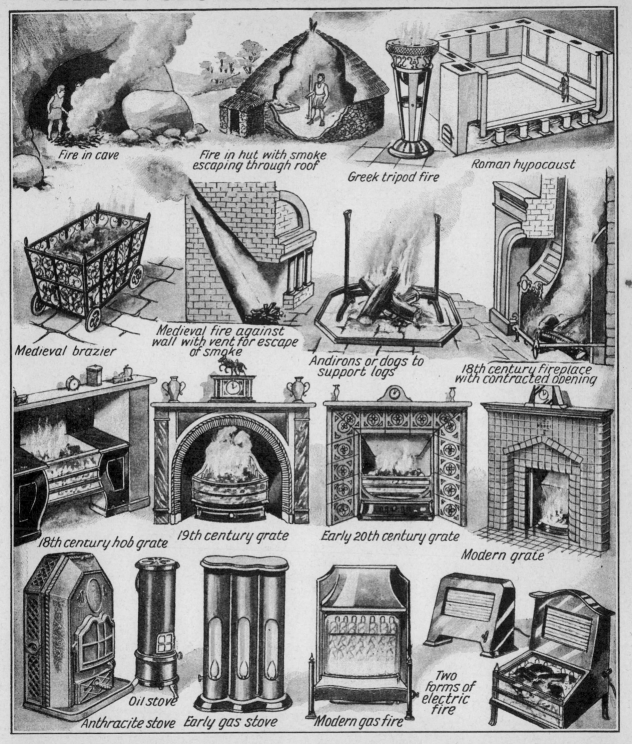

Fire in cave

Fire in hut with smoke escaping through roof

Greek tripod fire

Roman hypocaust

Medieval brazier

Medieval fire against wall with vent for escape of smoke

Andirons or dogs to support logs

18th century fireplace with contracted opening

18th century hob grate

19th century grate

Early 20th century grate

Modern grate

Anthracite stove

Oil stove

Early gas stove

Modern gas fire

Two forms of electric fire

In these pictures we see some of the stages by which man has, through the centuries, evolved a satisfactory method of heating his home in cold weather. When fires were first lighted in primitive man's dwelling the smoke must have been a great nuisance, and it continued so right down to the fourteenth or fifteenth century. Up to that time there were no chimneys, merely a vent in the roof or wall for the escape of the smoke. We see here the Greek brazier, the Roman hypocaust, the early fireplace with a vent to the outer wall for the escape of the smoke, and different stages in the improvement of the fireplace and grate. We see also a slow combustion stove in which anthracite is burned, gas fires, old and new, and the electric fire. The improvements of recent years have been in two principal directions. The first has been the conserving of the heat so that it should be used for the warming of the room, instead of the greater proportion escaping up the flue, as was the case with the old-fashioned grate. The other improvement has been the reduction of smoke and dirt

ARTIFICIAL LIGHT FROM TORCH TO SEARCHLIGHT

Fire · Firebrand · Torch · Shell lamp · Stone lamp · Pottery lamp · Hanging lamp · Standard lamp · Roman candlestick · Pricket candlestick · Bronze lamp · Clip candlestick · Rushlight in holder · Candelabra · Horn lantern · Benzine lamp · Argand lamp · Gas burner · Arc light · Acetylene lamp · Flood-lighting projector · Mantle burner · Searchlight · Filament lamp

In these pictures we see how man has tried to replace the light of the Sun at night when the sky has become dark. At first his fire gave him light. Then he took from it a burning brand to light him on his way, and later, having seen how fat burned when thrown on the fire, he learnt to make torches and candles of fat. He also, very early, invented the oil lamp, making it first of all of stone or chalk or clay, and later of pottery and metal. For a wick he used a rush. Some lamps were stood on stands. Candles were made by dipping the wick again and again in tallow. Rushlights were rushes dipped in tallow. A great advance with the lamp was the use of a circular wick with a glass chimney to increase the draught. Then came gas and electricity, with both the arc and the incandescent lamps. Gas received a fresh lease of life with the coming of the incandescent mantle. Acetylene gas is also used for lighting

THE STORY OF THE WHEEL FOR TEN THOUSAND YEARS

Hollowed tree trunk

Solid wheels

An early made up wheel

The origin of spokes

Egyptian wheel

Conical wagon wheel

Cylindrical wagon wheel

Modern wagon wheel

Railway coach wheel

Locomotive wheels

Bicycle wheel

Motor bus wheel

These pictures show the development of the wheel. No doubt man first used the round trunk of a tree as a roller for shifting heavy objects. Then he would hollow out the middle part of the trunk, and this gave the idea of an axle with wheels at the ends. Probably the first wheels were solid, cut out of one piece of wood. One day a broken wheel had to be repaired, and perhaps this gave the idea of making up the wheel from several pieces. Then to reduce its weight holes were cut out, suggesting the use of spokes. The Egyptians made wheels much like modern carriage wheels. In the 18th century there was much argument as to whether big wagon wheels should be conical or cylindrical, and for a time both were used. During the last century the development of the wheel has been rapid

THE EVOLUTION OF THE PRIVATE CARRIAGE

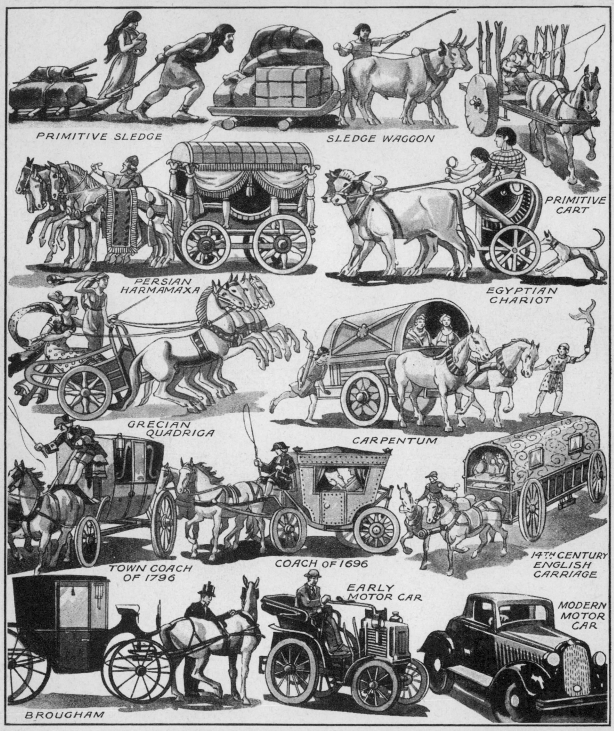

PRIMITIVE SLEDGE

SLEDGE WAGGON

PRIMITIVE CART

PERSIAN HARMAMAXA

EGYPTIAN CHARIOT

GRECIAN QUADRIGA

CARPENTUM

14TH CENTURY ENGLISH CARRIAGE

TOWN COACH OF 1796

COACH OF 1696

EARLY MOTOR CAR

MODERN MOTOR CAR

BROUGHAM

On this page we see a series of pictures which gives an idea of the slow evolution of the carriage from the early days when primitive man made a rough sledge, to the motor-car of to-day in which we can travel comfortably at sixty or seventy miles an hour. The invention of the wheel was a great step forward in the progress of the vehicle, and later the invention of the spring for carriages made travelling more comfortable than it had ever been before. Most of the early vehicles were very heavily-built, although the Egyptians seem to have had lightly-built chariots. The evolution of the waggon is a different story, as is also the development of the public vehicle. The pictures on this page are of private carriages, owned by individuals for their convenience. There certainly never was a time when so many people in civilised countries owned their own vehicle. The term "carriage folk" which formerly was an indication of social status, has no meaning now, for small tradesmen, clerks and farmers possess motor-cars.

THREE CENTURIES IN THE HISTORY OF THE CAB

Hackney Coach
1680

Hackney Coach
1800

The First Four-wheeled Cab 1823

London Cab
1823

The Coffin-cab
1830

Boulnois's Cab
1832

Parlour's Hansom
1887

Improved Hansom
1835

The First Hansom-cab
1834

Ordinary Hansom-cab

Early Electric-cab

Modern Taxi-cab

Here we see the story of the cab from its predecessor the hackney-carriage to the modern taxi-cab of to-day. Hackney coaches—heavy lumbering vehicles—first appeared in London at the beginning of the seventeenth century and continued till about 1840. But when the cabriolet, a name shortened to cab, appeared in 1823, its speed and lightness made it very popular, and it passed through several changes of form till it finally emerged as the hansom cab. This in the present century has been superseded by the motor-cab spoken of as a "taxi," because it is fitted with a taximeter for recording distance and fare. Perhaps one day this will give way to taxi-aeroplanes. Hackney coaches were named either from Hackney, where they plied or from the French haquenée, an ambling horse

QUEER FORERUNNERS OF THE MOTOR-CAR

These pictures show early examples of horseless carriages. Carts driven by sails have been used in China for centuries, and even to-day a truck on rails is sometimes driven by a sail. The windmill carriage was a development of the sailing chariot. The first idea for driving a vehicle with power inside itself was to use man power, as in the mechanical carriage of 1690, where the man at the back turned the wheels by treadles. Horse-power was also used as in the turntable coach of 1824, in which two horses in a car worked a rotating platform, the motion of which turned an axle by a band and pulleys. Another method was used in the cyclopede of 1829, a horse walking forward and turning an endless band which rotated the wheels. Another idea for a horseless carriage was a vehicle drawn along by a kite. Most practical engineers, however, looked to steam as the motive power for the horseless vehicle

EARLY STEAM CARRIAGES ON THE ROAD

GURNEY'S CARRIAGE 1827

JAMES'S CARRIAGE 1829

DANCE'S CARRIAGE 1833

GURNEY'S CARRIAGE 1831

HANCOCK'S CARRIAGE 1833

CHURCH'S COACH 1833

HILL'S COACH 1840

CARRETT'S CARRIAGE 1861

TANGYE'S CARRIAGE 1862

RANDOLPH'S CARRIAGE 1872

BOLLÉE'S CALASH 1878

BLACKMAN'S DOGCART 1880

In the first half of the eighteenth century there were attempts in many countries to adapt steam to the road vehicle, and in England particularly many such vehicles were constructed, and were used in London and other parts of the country. In some cases the engine and boiler were in the vehicle itself, while in other cases the engine trailed a carriage after it. The great difficulty however was the inefficiency of the steam-engine. Its size and weight were too great in proportion to its power. But as the steam engine was improved the possibilities of the steam carriage became greater, and even at the end of the nineteenth century and in the early years of the present century steam competed with the internal combustion engine   But it was not long before the   engine showed its supremacy for all the lighter forms of vehicles, and steam became obsolete except for certain types of very heavy wagons and lorries

THE QUEER BEGINNINGS OF THE RAILWAY ENGINE

FIRST LOCOMOTIVE 1803

BLENKINSOP 1812

PUFFING BILLY 1813

BRUNTON'S ENGINE 1813

STEPHENSONS FIRST ENGINE 1814

STEPHENSONS KILLINGWORTH ENGINE 1816

LOCOMOTIVE Nº1 1825

ROCKET 1829

TWIN SISTERS 1827

INVICTA 1830

NOVELTY 1829

PLANET 1830

In these pictures we see the early evolution of the locomotive. The pioneer locomotive was that of Richard Trevithick, built in 1803, a strange-looking affair with large gear wheels, but nevertheless an engine that travelled with smooth wheels on smooth rails. Despite its success, however, Blenkinsop made his locomotive to travel by means of a rack rail and cogwheel. Puffing Billy, built by William Hedley, for a colliery, was a great success, and ran till 1872. Brunton's strange locomotive, which had hind legs, was not successful, and it was George Stephenson who made the railway engine really practicable. His Rocket, built for the Liverpool and Manchester Railway, was a great triumph. It beat several rivals, including the Novelty, and established the true principles of the locomotive.

THE DEVELOPMENT OF THE MODERN LOCOMOTIVE

ATLAS 1836

NORTH STAR 1837

GREAT WESTERN 1846

CORNWALL 1847

L&S.W. VICTORIA 1859

TANK ENGINE 1870

MIDLAND EXPRESS 1885

NORTH EASTERN 1901

ROYAL SCOT 1933

STREAM-LINED ENGINE

In these pictures we see how the locomotive has developed from the early types of nearly a century ago. It will be noticed that the principle and general form of the railway engine is still the same, although there are signs now that a great change is coming, and that the locomotives of the future will be stream-lined and have very much the form and shape of a torpedo or racing car. Several countries are experimenting with such engines. Just as in early days England was the pioneer of the locomotive, so from the beginning she has always kept well ahead, and the modern engines which have recently been put upon the various British lines are the finest products of their kind to be seen in the world to-day. When the London, Midland and Scottish locomotive Royal Scot was sent across the Atlantic and toured both Canada and the United States, it called forth the loudest praise of the transatlantic engineers, who admired not only its capabilities but its beautiful lines and magnificent workmanship.

THE STORY OF THE SHIP FROM DUG-OUT TO LINER

It was probably a floating log that first gave man the idea of a boat. While swimming he found the log supported him, and then probably straddled it, and in that way crossed river or lake. Later a number of tree trunks were tied together to form a raft (picture 1), and then came the dug-out canoe (2), the trunk of a tree with a place hollowed out with stone adze or fire. Such dug-outs are still in use among primitive peoples in South America and elsewhere. Then came the sail (3), which may have been suggested by a man finding that the wind blowing his skin cloak helped the boat along. Gradually the sailing boat was developed, the Egyptians having galleys with large sails assisted by rowers (4). The Romans improved on these (5), and the Vikings did still better with their sailing ships (6). Sailing ships like that of Columbus (7) performed marvels, and they were constantly being improved. The East Indiaman (8) of the eighteenth century was succeeded by the clipper of the next century (9), and at last steam was used as an auxiliary (10). Then ships were driven entirely by steam (11) by means of paddle wheels, and at last came the modern steamship with its screw propellers driven by turbines (12). A steady increase in size has followed the other developments

NEARLY TWO CENTURIES OF STEAMSHIPS

HULL'S PADDLE TUG 1737

DE JOUFFROY'S STEAMBOAT 1783

FITCHS OARED BOAT 1786

SYMINGTONS CHARLOTTE DUNDAS 1802.

SYMINGTONS TWIN BOAT 1788

FULTON'S CLERMONT 1807

BELL'S COMET 1812

SAVANNAH 1819

SIRIUS 1838

GREAT WESTERN 1838

BRITANNIA 1840

GREAT BRITAIN 1845

MAURETANIA 1907

On this page we can trace the development of the steamship from its early and humble beginnings in the eighteenth century. The first steamboat for which a patent was taken out was that of Jonathan Hulls, shown in the first picture, but the engine took up so much room that it could be used only as a tug. Nothing very practical was done for nearly half a century, and then the development of the steamship began in earnest. We see the early attempts of the French and English, and we see also Robert Fulton's *Clermont*, an American production. But Fulton had obtained his ideas from a close study of French and English models. The *Savannah* crossed the Atlantic in 1819, the first boat fitted with a steam engine. But she steamed only a few miles at the beginning and end of her voyage. The rest of the journey she sailed. The first real steamships to cross the Atlantic were two English boats, the *Sirius* and the *Great Western*, which arrived at New York within a few hours of one another. From then till now progress has been rapid, and steamships are ever-increasing in size

HOW MAN HAS TOLD THE TIME THROUGH THE AGES

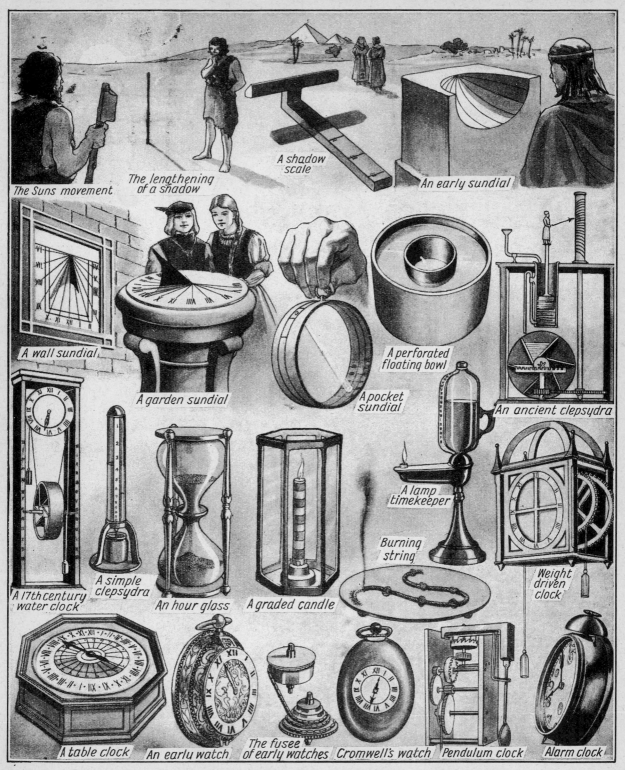

The Suns movement

The lengthening of a shadow

A shadow scale

An early sundial

A wall sundial

A garden sundial

A pocket sundial

A perforated floating bowl

An ancient clepsydra

A 17th century water clock

A simple clepsydra

An hour glass

A graded candle

Burning string

A lamp timekeeper

Weight driven clock

A table clock

An early watch

The fusee of early watches

Cromwell's watch

Pendulum clock

Alarm clock

These pictures show the evolution of the clock, from the far-off days when man first noted the passing of time by watching the Sun's movement in the heavens. Then he noticed that the shadows lengthened as the Sun sank, and the Ancient Egyptians told the time by shadow scales, in which the shadow of a bar passed along a scale as the Sun rose or sank. Sundials followed, and many exist to-day. Of course, sundials have to be adjusted to different latitudes. Many other devices have been used for telling the time, such as a bowl slowly filling with water, a dial worked by a float in water, and a burning candle, lamp or string. At last came the clock

Book 7

AMAZING ADVENTURES *in* SCIENCE

HOW HEAT CAUSES A GAS AND A SOLID TO EXPAND

If we take an ordinary rubber balloon and blow into it we can fill it out to a certain size. Then, if we take this balloon and hold it near a warm radiator or some distance from a fire, being careful not to go too near, we shall find that the balloon will gradually get bigger and bigger, and if we hold it in the warmth too long it may even burst. The reason is that the molecules of air in the balloon are made to move to and fro more and more rapidly, and as they require increased space in which to do this, the air in the balloon occupies a larger volume than it did when it was cooler

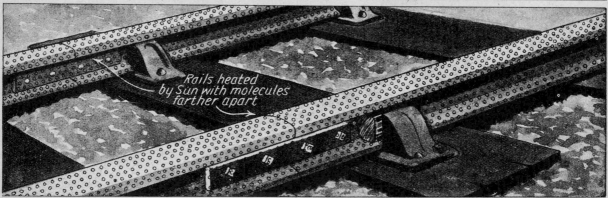

We have probably noticed that the rails on which the train runs are not fitted close together—there is always a space between the individual rails. This is to allow for the expansion of the metal when the hot sun shines upon it. If we look at the track on a hot day we shall find that the ends of the rails are much closer together than they are on a cold and frosty day. The metal expands as it gets warmer because the molecules of which it is composed are vibrating with increased motion, and as they require more space for their movement the great mass of metal requires more room, and so increases in size

WHY HEAT MAKES THINGS BIGGER

Heat is really energy and the energy takes the form of motion among the molecules of which a body is made up. This is one of the remarkable discoveries of modern times. It used to be thought in the olden days that heat was a substance like air or water which got into a body, but we know better nowadays. One of the various and interesting results of heat is described on this page

WE must all of us be aware that when things get hot they almost invariably get bigger; or, in other words, they occupy more space.

We see this in the thermometer. As the temperature rises and the mercury or alcohol in the bulb gets warmer, it occupies more space, and therefore rises in the tube.

The same thing is true of a solid and of a gas. When the railway men lay the track and place the metals on which the train is to run end to end, they always leave a certain amount of space between the ends of the rails to allow for the expansion of the metal when the Sun shines upon it in hot weather.

If they did not do this, the result would be that on some very warm summer day the rails all along the line would expand, and as there would not be room for them to extend lengthwise, they would have to buckle up to some extent and the track would then become dangerous.

In regard to a gas, if we blow up a child's rubber balloon to about half its usual capacity and close the opening, we can expand the balloon a great deal more by holding it near a hot radiator or some little distance from a fire. The gas inside the balloon gets hot and expands, puffing out the balloon more and more as it does so. The increase of the space occupied owing to the heat is more manifest in the case of the air inside the balloon than in that of the steel rail or even the alcohol of the thermometer.

Now why does a substance need more space as it gets hotter? In the old days men of science thought that heat was a material like water, and that a body increased in size as it got hotter for the same reason that a dry sponge gets bigger when it is immersed in water. They supposed that the substance of the neat was added to the substance of the other material and so caused more space to be necessary for the combination of the two.

We know better in these days. Heat is not a substance at all; it is merely a state of matter. All substances are made up of molecules, tiny particles.

Now, although an object like a steel rail may appear to be very still, the molecules of which it is made up are really moving to and fro, or in other words they are vibrating. When a substance becomes hotter through combustion, or when the hot sun shines upon it, the vibrations of the molecules are increased; that is, they are moving to and fro much more rapidly. And the movement increases more and more as the material becomes more heated.

This increased movement requires more space as the molecules are driven farther and farther asunder, and so the whole body which the molecules make up has to increase in volume. If it is a solid it increases in length and breadth and thickness, and if it is a liquid or a gas it increases in volume; that is, in all directions where it is free to move.

If the heat continues to increase, the movement of the molecules becomes so great that the force of cohesion is at last overcome and the heated body, if a solid, loses its rigidity and becomes liquid. If it is still further heated, it will cease to be a liquid and become a gas, and enormous heat like that found on the Sun may even break up the molecules of matter.

We speak of various bodies as being good or bad conductors of heat. What do we mean by this? Well, the spread of heat through a body such, for example, as a bar of iron is due to a gradual communication to the molecules in the bar, of the vibratory motion from the heated part to the remainder. By saying that a body or substance is a good conductor of heat, we mean that it is one which readily takes up and transmits the vibratory motion from particle to particle, while a bad conductor is one in which the motion is transmitted only with difficulty.

This simple experiment enables us to see that heat increases the volume of a liquid. When we put the thermometer into the hot water of the bath immediately the alcohol or mercury in the bulb increases in volume, and we see it expand and run up the glass tube, as shown in the right-hand picture

DIFFERENT KINDS OF ELECTRIC CELLS

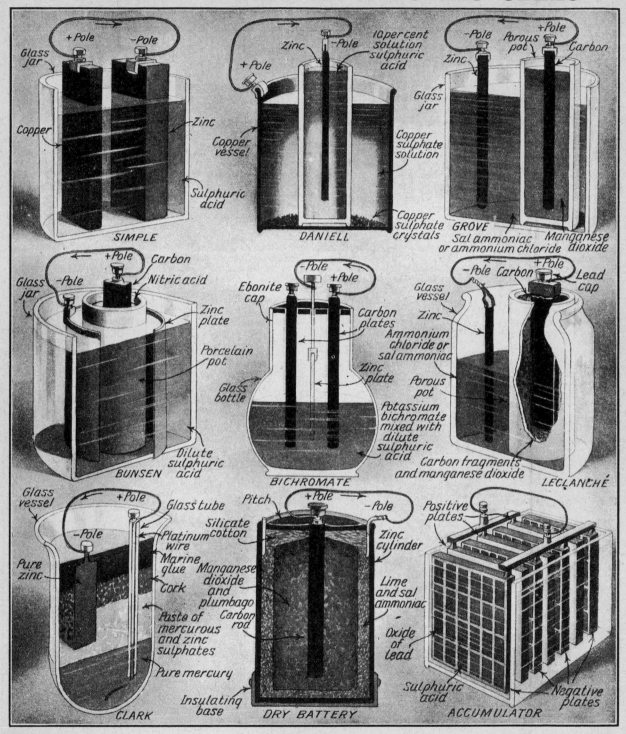

An electric cell consists of two metals, or one metal and carbon, immersed in a liquid which acts chemically on one of the metals, the chemical action being transformed into electric energy. There are many different kinds of cells, adapted to different purposes. Here we see some of the more familiar cells used in general practice, with the substances of which they are composed and the positive and negative poles marked. The zinc is always the negative pole and the electric current flows through the copper wire from the positive to the negative pole. Some scientists, however, now say the flow is in the opposite direction. Different shaped vessels are used for these cells. In an accumulator there are two lead plates or two sets of lead plates in sulphuric acid. One plate or set is partially transformed into lead peroxide by passing an electric current through the cell. So long as the plates differ the accumulator acts as an electric cell and will furnish a current. When it is run down by passing a current through it, one of the plates or sets will again be reduced to lead, and the other plate or set oxidised to lead peroxide. Then the accumulator will again act as an electric cell

WHAT HAPPENS IN AN ELECTRIC CELL

There are many different kinds of electric cells, but all are on the same principle. They consist of two metal plates immersed in weak acid and the chemical action which results is transformed into electrical energy which can be conducted away by means of a copper wire. Sometimes a plate of carbon is used in place of one of the metals. Here we read something about electric cells and batteries

WHAT is Electricity? Nobody can say except that it is a form of energy, and the latest discoveries of scientists suggest that it is really the basis of all matter; or, in other words, that the atoms of which all substances consist are really made up of particles of electricity.

But although we cannot fully understand the real nature of electricity, we can all make use of it in a variety of ways, and few homes to-day fail to use electricity in some form or other. If we do not have electric fires and electric-cookers and vacuum cleaners and telephones, at any rate we have electric light or wireless: and if we have none of these conveniences we probably use a portable flash-lamp, the light of which is provided by electricity.

When electricity is wanted on a large scale, as for driving a railway or lighting a city, it is produced by a generator driven by a steam or water turbine;

but for various domestic purposes such as electric bells, wireless sets, and so on, we use batteries or accumulators, of which there are many different forms, suited to different purposes.

The battery method of producing electricity is too expensive for use on a large scale, and that is why we produce it mechanically at power stations. In a battery the electricity is produced by chemical action; in other words, chemical energy is changed into electrical energy just as by a generator at a power station mechanical energy is changed into electrical energy.

We speak of "generating" electricity, but, of course, this is not a strictly correct term. Electricity cannot be generated, for it already exists in the structure of all matter. What we do by means of a battery or generator is to rearrange the protons and electrons of the atoms, and cause them to move in certain directions.

A battery is made up of two or more electric cells, and some of the chief forms of cell are shown on the next page. The simplest cell consists of a vessel containing an acid which acts chemically on some metal immersed in it, the chemical action being transformed into electrical energy.

For example, if a plate of copper and another of zinc be placed in dilute sulphuric acid, the acid acts on the zinc plate, dissolving part of it and producing electrical energy equal to the amount of chemical energy expended. If the two plates be joined by a copper wire, forming what is called an electric circuit, the electricity will pass as a current along the wire. It is merely conducted or guided by the wire, and does not pass through it as water does through a pipe.

All electric cells are on this principle, though different substances are used.

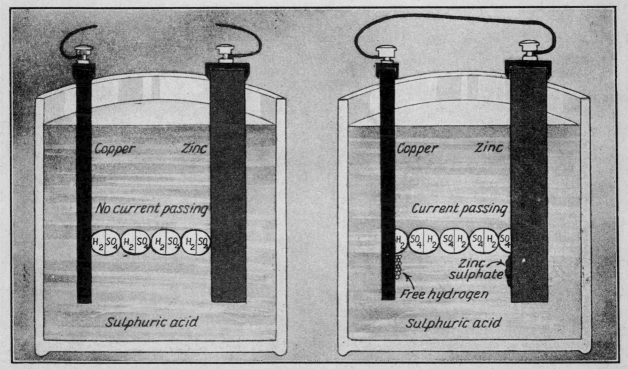

Here we see what goes on in an electric cell. In the first cell the wires are not joined up and so the circuit is broken. The molecules of sulphuric acid, therefore, remain unchanged. Each molecule consists of two atoms of hydrogen, represented as H_2, one of sulphur S, and four of oxygen, O_4. Directly the wires are joined and the circuit completed, as in the second cell, chemical action begins. An atom of zinc combines with the sulphur and oxygen atoms of the acid molecule forming zinc sulphate and freeing the atoms of hydrogen, which thereupon combine with the atoms of sulphur and oxygen in the next molecule, freeing that molecule's atoms of hydrogen. So the chemical action goes on till we come to the last molecule of acid in the series. Here there are no sulphur and oxygen atoms left to combine with the liberated hydrogen atoms, and so they collect on the copper plate

HOW INFRA-RED RAYS MAY SAVE THE SHIP

Experiments attended with some success have been carried out at sea by means of a new system of photography, which it is hoped will lead to greater safety in foggy weather. It is found that in many cases the infra-red rays which lie beyond the red rays of the spectrum when light is broken up, will pierce the fog. Our eyes cannot see things by means of these invisible rays, but special photographic plates are made sensitive to them, and it is possible to take a photograph through the fog showing what lies beyond. We see in this picture how in the experiments a ship has been able to take a clear photograph of another ship coming towards it through a fog, when those on board were unable to see anything. Unfortunately, the infra-red rays will not pierce all fogs, their success varying with the size of the water particles that make up the fog. Perhaps one day this difficulty will be overcome. A special camera takes and develops the photographs almost instantaneously so that the oncoming vessel can be seen within one minute of the exposure

THE WONDER OF THE INFRA-RED RAYS

The invisible infra-red rays which are found beyond the red end of the spectrum when white light is broken up are being used for more and more purposes. Here we read of a curious way in which they are being utilised to reveal secrets of the past that have remained hidden for many centuries

WHEN white light is broken up by a prism it is found to consist of the seven colours, violet, indigo, blue, green, yellow, orange, red. We can see these colours, which are due to rays of light of varying wavelengths.

But there are other rays which form part of the Sun's light which cannot be seen, but are just as real as the others. Some of these are beyond the violet rays, and are known as ultra-violet, while others are at the other end, beyond the red rays, and are known as infra-red, "infra" meaning "below" or "lower down."

Of course it is only in recent times that these invisible rays have been known to scientists, who are now making much use of them. It has been found that the ultra-violet rays are very good for health, and so patients in hospitals and elsewhere are treated with these rays and get great benefit from them.

The infra-red rays, also, are used for health purposes, but recently a new use has been discovered and it is found that things can be photographed clearly with their aid which would be very indistinct or not come out at all with only ordinary light rays.

For instance, airmen can take photographs of distant places that are quite invisible to the eye, or to the ordinary photographic plate, for by means of plates that are sensitive to infra-red rays the distant landscapes come out quite distinctly.

Further, as we see elsewhere, a hot object in a dark room which is quite invisible can be photographed clearly on a plate sensitive to infra-red rays.

The infra-red rays, like the ultra-violet, are valuable in medical treatment. They have proved beneficial in the treatment of rheumatic patients, and it is interesting to know that woollen fabric allows the infra-red rays to pass through it much more easily than a cotton fabric, or a cloth made up of a mixture of wool and cotton. The same is true of the passage of ultra-violet light.

Sunbaths, in which the Sun's rays play upon the bare skin, are very beneficial, for then the ultra-violet and infra-red rays are not impeded at all.

The latest use to which the infra-red rays have been put is a curious and interesting one. They have been used for wresting secrets 5,000 years old from ancient documents.

Experiments have been made by the British Museum authorities in photographing old Egyptian documents in which the writing was so faded as to be almost invisible and quite undecipherable.

When such documents were photographed on a plate sensitive to infra-red rays, the faded and invisible writing came out as distinctly as though it were written boldly in black ink. An example of such a photograph is given on this page.

Why is it that the lost writing is thus restored to sight? Well, when an ink or dye fades it means that the rays of light have set up certain chemical changes in the colouring matter, and the changed ink no longer reflects the light as it did when it was fresh upon the papyrus or leather.

But although the writing may have faded so that it is quite invisible, the material of the ink has not disappeared. It has merely been changed in chemical character, and while the changed material will not reflect ordinary light, it does reflect the infra-red rays, so that they strike upon the plate. The ordinary light is usually filtered out by means of screens, so that the infra-red rays can be unimpeded and have full play.

An infra-red photograph of part of the Egyptian Book of the Dead. The writing had faded so as to be undecipherable, but the infra-red rays were reflected by the faded writing, and gave a bold representation on the plate.

THE VARIED DESIGNS MADE BY MAGNETS

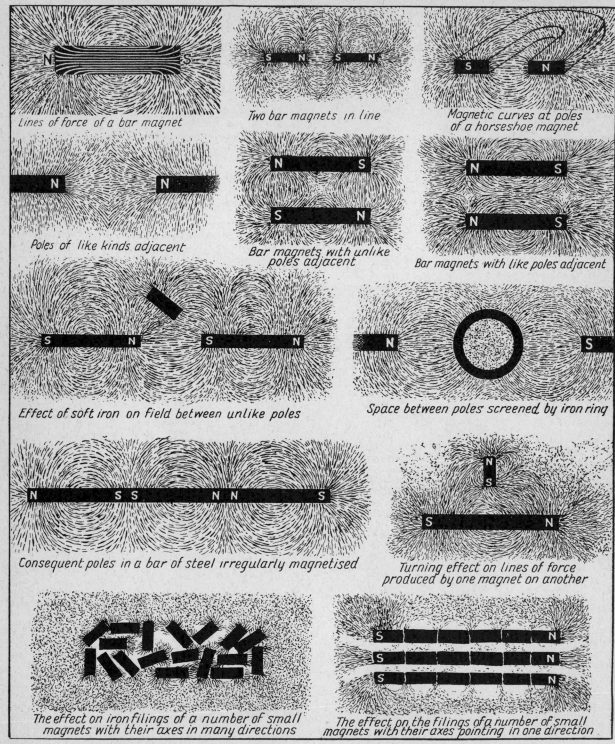

Lines of force of a bar magnet

Two bar magnets in line

Magnetic curves at poles of a horseshoe magnet

Poles of like kinds adjacent

Bar magnets with unlike poles adjacent

Bar magnets with like poles adjacent

Effect of soft iron on field between unlike poles

Space between poles screened by iron ring

Consequent poles in a bar of steel irregularly magnetised

Turning effect on lines of force produced by one magnet on another

The effect on iron filings of a number of small magnets with their axes in many directions

The effect on the filings of a number of small magnets with their axes pointing in one direction

The space all round a magnet which is affected by the magnetic force is called the magnetic field. The lines or directions which the magnetic force takes can be seen by placing paper over a magnet or magnets and dusting the paper all over with very fine iron filings. These settle down into designs or figures, which depend upon the lines of force. To assist the settling of the filings the paper should be tapped very lightly. In the first picture the outside lines of force can be seen continued through the magnet. When two magnets are brought together the lines of force vary according to whether like or unlike poles are adjacent. When a flat iron ring is placed between two unlike poles, no magnetic curves are seen inside the ring. If a steel bar is irregularly magnetised by being touched with magnets at different points, it practically becomes a series of several magnets. The magnets are shown black, but are supposed to be under the paper

THE MARVEL OF THE ELECTRO-MAGNET

The electro-magnet is a marvellous device on which many of our modern electrical machines depend for their success. It owes its value to a remarkable property of iron which is described here, and without which the electro-magnet as we know it would be impossible

WE all know that we can change a bar of iron or steel into a magnet by stroking it in one direction with another magnet. It takes much longer to make the steel into a magnet than the iron, but, on the other hand, the iron loses its magnetism much more quickly than the steel.

Now there is another way in which we can change a bar of iron or steel into a magnet and that is by passing a current of electricity along a coil of insulated copper wire in the hollow of which the bar of iron is placed. This magnetises the bar more powerfully than any other method.

But there is a very curious thing about this. If the bar be soft iron, that is pure or almost pure iron, the bar will be a magnet only so long as the electric current is flowing along the wire. Cut off the current and the iron immediately ceases to be a magnet. On the other hand, if the bar is of steel it will become magnetised much more slowly, but when the current is turned off it will still remain a magnet.

This property of iron is of the greatest service to mankind. We have already seen how valuable to us is the property of water which causes it to expand as it is about to freeze so that ice is lighter than water and floats in the liquid. Were it not for this the seas in the temperate regions would become frozen solid and countries would become ice-locked and uninhabitable.

Well, in the same way this curious property of iron, which causes it when pure to become easily magnetised and demagnetised and when it is hardened with a small portion of carbon to become permanently magnetised, though with more difficulty, is of untold value in electrical engineering. Without it our electric bells and telegraphs and many more elaborate machines would not work at all. We can see this in electric bell, the telegraph, the electric light, and so on.

The great magnets for lifting and loading masses of iron would be useless if the magnet could not be made and unmade at will by the turning on and off of the current as required.

It was this discovery by Humphry Davy of how to make the electro-magnet by passing a current along an insulated copper wire winding round an iron core that started the great science of electrical engineering and led to so many of the wonders with which we are familiar to-day.

William Sturgeon first used the name electro-magnet, and he did much to apply the discovery of Davy to practical uses. His first electro-magnet was in the form of a horse-shoe, which was made from a rod of iron a foot long and half an inch in diameter. Round this he coiled a stout copper wire with only 18 turns.

When the current from a single electric cell was passed along the wire, the iron became a magnet strong enough to lift a weight of nine pounds. With a more powerful battery, however, the magnet lifted fifty pounds.

In addition to being under the control of the current, so that when the circuit is made the iron becomes a magnet and when it is broken the iron is demagnetised, the electro-magnet has the further great advantage that it can be controlled from a distance by means of a key or switch.

In making an electro-magnet it is necessary to insulate the wire and to see that the iron that is to be magnetised does not touch the wire of the spiral, for in that case the current would short-circuit, that is, take a short cut through the iron from one turn of the wire to the next instead of going round and round the spiral. Some enormously powerful electro-magnets are now being made and used.

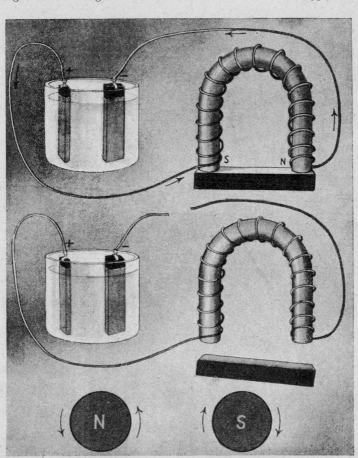

These pictures show the principle of the electro-magnet. When a bar of soft iron, either straight or bent into a horseshoe, is placed inside a coil of copper wire and a current is passed along the wire, the iron becomes a magnet, as in the upper picture. Directly the current is cut off, as in the lower picture, the iron ceases to be a magnet. Were it not for this the electric bell and the telegraph would not work. Which end of the magnet becomes the north pole and which the south depends upon the direction in which the wire is coiled round and the current passes. If we look at the north pole the current is always passing round anti-clockwise, and if we look at the south pole it is passing clockwise, as we see at the bottom of this drawing

DIFFERENT WAYS IN WHICH THINGS BURN

An explosion of gunpowder

A furnace burning fiercely

The fire in the grate

A burning candle

The slow-combustion stove

A smouldering stack

Iron rusting

A stack of coal oxidising very slowly

Athletes in whose body carbon is burning

Burning or combustion is really the combination of a substance with the gas oxygen, which forms part of the atmosphere. It is not always accompanied by flame, and the burning may be fast or slow. When gunpowder explodes, the burning is very rapid. It is slower in the locomotive furnace and still less rapid in the fire of our grates. When a candle is alight it is burning, but with less heat than the fire. In an anthracite stove the burning goes on slowly, and still more slowly when a haystack gets hot and burns spontaneously because it was stacked when damp. The rusting of iron is really slow burning, and a pile of coal in the open air or cellar is continually burning at a very slow rate, for the oxygen of the air is combining with it. When we breathe burning is going on, for the carbon of our body is combining with the oxygen of the air, and the faster we move and breathe the faster the burning goes on

THE MYSTERY OF THE BURNING GLASS

Even a small convex lens or magnifying glass will concentrate the Sun's rays so that they become powerful enough in summer time to set light to paper or wood. This device, on a large scale, has even been suggested as a weapon of defence, and there are stories that it was so used in ancient times. Here we read about the burning glass and the explanation of its strange power

MOST of us know that if we hold a magnifying lens, such as an ordinary reading glass, so as to catch the Sun's rays, a very bright point of light will be projected or thrown beyond the glass and that this will have very great heat, much greater than the rays of the Sun unassisted by the glass. Why is this?

Well, the reading glass is a double-convex lens, that is, it is a lens in which there is a bulge outward on both sides. The rays of the Sun strike one side of this lens and then pass through the glass to the other side, but in the passage the rays are bent at an angle and so the parallel rays which strike the glass at different parts of its surface are all brought to a focus, or meeting-place, at one point. This can be seen clearly in the upper picture on this page.

Naturally, when all the different rays are brought to act upon one point, there is much greater heat there than at any point where only one or two rays strike. The result is that when a reading-glass is used in this way, it becomes a burning-glass and paper, or even wood can be set alight by the action of the concentrated heat.

Summer Experiments

In summer-time some interesting experiments can be performed with a reading-glass in this way. They had better be carried out in the open-air so that there may be no danger of setting light to anything of value indoors. Boy scouts and campers out, for example, can light a camp fire made up of sticks and dry leaves by merely focussing upon one part of it the Sun's rays from a magnifying lens.

It is important to remember the power of the Sun's rays when concentrated in this way. Rooms have been set on fire before now and much damage done, by the Sun shining through a window and being focussed by a glass bottle or jug full of water upon a book or table-cloth. The vessel of water acts as a burning-glass and sets fire to the inflammable material on which the rays are directed.

That is why it is always important that a glass bottle or jug of water should never be left in an exposed position near a window through which the Sun is shining or is likely to shine.

The same result can be obtained by using a concave mirror. The parallel rays of the Sun strike this at its various points and are reflected at an angle so that they are all focussed or concentrated upon a single point, and great heat results.

We are not certain who first discovered this power of convex lenses and concave mirrors. According to tradition it was that great scientist

When the Sun's rays which reach the surface of a magnifying lens in parallel lines are focussed upon wood, paper, or other inflammable material they are powerful enough, on a hot summer day, to set the material alight

Even a glass jug or bottle of water in the direct line of the Sun's rays will act as a burning glass, and fires have been caused on many occasions in this way. Of course, the Sun is so far off that all its rays really reach us in parallel lines

of ancient times, Archimedes. The story goes that when the Romans, under the Consul Marcellus, besieged the city of Syracuse in Sicily in the year 214 B.C. their ships were set alight by means of burning glasses invented by Archimedes, who at the time was 75 years of age.

The historian, Edward Gibbon, tells us another story of how Proclus, the philosopher, destroyed the Gothic vessels in the harbour of Constantinople by the same means. "A machine was fixed on the walls of the city," he says, "consisting of a hexagon mirror of polished brass, with many smaller and movable polygons to receive and reflect the rays of the meridian sun; and a consuming flame was directed to the distance, perhaps of two hundred feet."

Although the most reliable ancient historians of these periods do not refer to the burning-glasses of Archimedes or the burning mirrors of Proclus, Gibbon thinks the stories are quite likely to be true. It is more reasonable, he thinks, to regard the traditions as facts, than to suppose that they were imagined by monks of later days.

A Great Burning Glass

If these ancient scientists really discovered the power of burning glasses and mirrors, then their knowledge was afterwards lost for centuries. We find no further reference to such devices till the sixteenth and seventeenth centuries, when John Napier, the Scotsman who invented logarithms, mentions them as useful for defence. The biggest ever constructed was made by an Englishman named Parker about 1800. It cost £700, and with it gold, silver, copper, iron, steel, topaz, emerald, flint, cornelian and pumice-stone were fused or melted. It was afterwards taken to Pekin, but what happened to it in the end is not known.

In Paris there used to be a time signal which consisted of a gun that was fired at noon by the Sun's rays focussed through a magnifying lens fixed in the necessary position.

MEASURING THE SPEED OF SOUND

Sound travels at different rates through different substances, and men have measured these different speeds. Here we see the speed of sound in air being measured by a group of scientists more than a hundred years ago. The scientists were divided into two groups, one at Montlhéry and the other at Villejuif in France, a distance of 61,047 feet apart. Each group was provided with a chronometer and two cannon. Twelve shots were fired at intervals of ten minutes from each station, and each group noted the number of seconds which elapsed between the sight of the flash and the arrival of the sound   The light was seen practically instantaneously, but the sound took $54\frac{9}{10}$ seconds to travel the distance. The scientists, therefore, concluded that sound travels at 1,118 feet per second

In water sound travels more quickly than in air. Two scientists named Colladon and Sturm proved this by an experiment on the Lake of Geneva nearly a century ago. They were seated in boats, one at Thonon, the other on the other side of the lake. Sound was produced by striking a hammer on a bell immersed in the water at one station, while at the other station a large speaking-trumpet was let down into the water   A sheet of metal was placed over the large opening of the speaking-trumpet, and this vibrated when the wave sounds struck upon it after transmission through the water. The observer with the trumpet held a chronometer, and he learned the instant when the bell was struck by a flash produced in the other boat by firing some magnesium powder. This powder was ignited by the lowering of a lighted match attached to the hammer which struck the bell. The distance of the stations apart was 44,237 feet, and this was traversed by the sound of the bell in $9\frac{1}{4}$ seconds, which gave 4,706 feet per second for the speed of sound in water

SOUND WAVES THAT WE CAN SEE

The wonders of science never cease and in the achievement of many of these photography plays a large part. Who would ever have thought that the waves in the air set up by sounds would be photographed so as to be seen by our eyes, yet, as we read here, this wonder has been actually accomplished

WE all like to stand on the beach or look over the side of a boat and watch the waves move up and down on the water and travel along. But although we know that sound is the result of waves in the atmosphere striking our ear-drums, we do not usually think of these waves as being visible. Yet there are times when sound waves in the atmosphere can be seen.

Early in the present century an American scientist was standing on Vesuvius during an eruption. Every few seconds there was an explosion and lava and rocky fragments were thrown out of the crater. As the professor watched the smoke and dust rise from the volcano he saw a thin ring of light move upwards rapidly from the crater and suddenly disappear. He continued to watch, and at each explosion the same phenomenon was seen. A luminous ring shot out of the volcano disappearing immediately. These rings moved up far more quickly than the solid matter.

A few years later the same scientist saw the rings of light during an eruption of Etna. He described them, and explained that the flashing arcs, as he termed them, were really visible sound waves.

The same kind of thing was witnessed during the Great War. When the big guns were fired, curved bands of light were often seen to sweep across the sky. They looked very much like the ripples which we see when we throw a pebble into a pond. These also were visible sound waves.

Attempts were made to photograph both the volcanic sound waves and those from guns, but without success. Sound waves have, however, been photographed, and show up clearly in the case of a rifle bullet flying through the air. A photograph was taken with an exposure of one-millionth of a second, and the light rays passing through a segment of the air which had been compressed by the flying bullet, were distinctly recorded in the train of the bullet.

The reason for the visibility of sound waves in the circumstances mentioned is that air bends or refracts light rays according to its density. The light passing through the condensed air which is rapidly expanding to resume its old volume, bends the rays of light so markedly that they are visible to the eye or the camera.

When a silencer is used in firing the bullet from the rifle and a photograph is taken, no sound waves are then visible on the plate, for the simple reason that the sound being reduced there are no waves to make their appearance on the sensitized film.

The photographing of sound waves in the manner described is of great interest as a scientific triumph, but it is of more than theoretical interest, for by study of these photographs scientists hope to be able to deal with the loud noise made by a moving aeroplane and to introduce methods or machinery that shall make the aircraft practically silent.

The noise of the aeroplane, it has been discovered, comes from three different sources. One is the popping of the exhaust, and this can be abolished by a silencer similar to that used with a gun.

Then there is the churning of the air by the propeller, which is responsible for about a third of the noise. This can be lessened by using gears, for it is a fact that after a certain point has been reached the aeroplane's speed is not increased by increasing the number of the propeller's revolutions per minute.

Finally, there is the noise known as "flutter," which is similar to the sound made by a flag in the breeze. The blades of the propeller create a hurricane and the aeroplane as it moves through this is set fluttering in all its parts, and this makes quite a large proportion of the total noise caused by a moving aeroplane. Devices to silence the flutter sounds are being thought out and these instantaneous photographs of sound waves are contributing a good deal of help in the work.

A photograph of a bullet just after it has left the muzzle of the rifle, showing the sound-waves which it causes as it whirls through the air. The photograph was given an exposure of only one-millionth of a second

An instantaneous photograph of a bullet just after it has left the rifle's muzzle, when fired through a silencer. It will be noticed that the sound-waves seen in the upper photograph are entirely absent here

HOW SOUNDS ARE MADE VISIBLE TO THE EYE

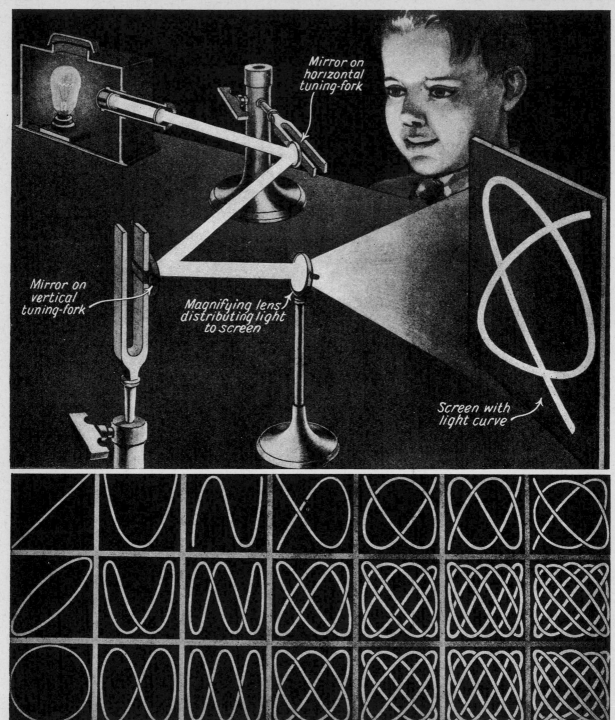

It is possible to make sounds visible to the eye, and the method is shown on this page. In the upper part of the picture we see two tuning-forks to which have been attached small mirrors. One of these forks is placed in a stand horizontally, while the other stands vertically. A powerful beam of light is made to shine into the mirror of the horizontal tuning-fork, and the vertical fork is so placed that the light is reflected into its mirror from the first mirror, and thence passed through a lens so as to shine upon a screen. If now the horizontal tuning-fork be sounded while the second fork remains at rest, the light on the screen becomes a beautiful luminous streak. When the vertical tuning-fork is also sounded in unison with the other, the straight line of light on the screen becomes a bright curve. If, now, a piece of wax be fastened to one of the tuning-forks so that there is a slight difference in its vibration, the luminous figure on the screen will be changed and pass through many variations. When there is a difference of an octave between the tuning-forks the curves on the screen become very complex. The lower part of this picture shows some of the remarkable variations that are presented

Book 8

The SEVEN WONDERS
of the MODERN WORLD

HOW A MICROSCOPE MAKES THINGS BIG

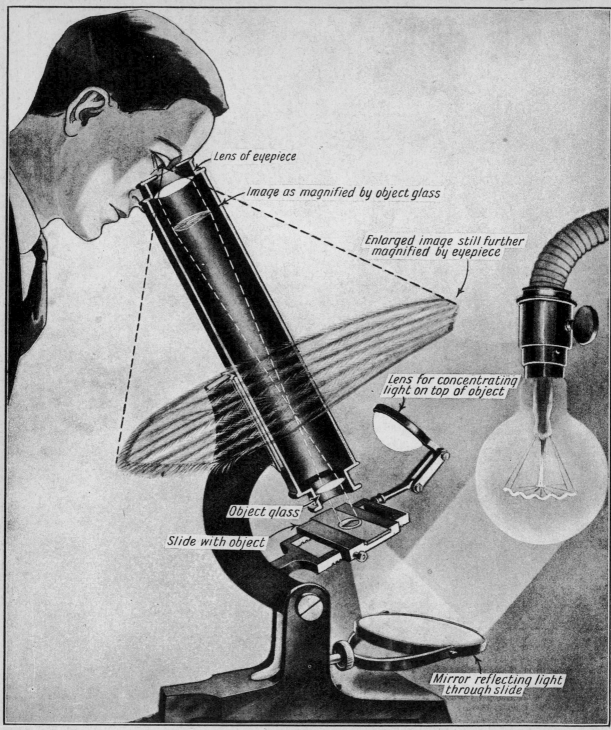

Lens of eyepiece

Image as magnified by object glass

Enlarged image still further magnified by eyepiece

Lens for concentrating light on top of object

Object glass

Slide with object

Mirror reflecting light through slide

This picture shows how a microscope makes small objects appear very large. The object to be magnified is in a glass slide, and this is placed on a stage and illuminated from above or below, according to whether it is opaque or transparent. In this case the object is a tiny insect's wing, and being transparent is illuminated from below. Rays of light pass from it to a magnifying lens known as the object glass. The curved lens causes the rays to be bent at an angle and to cross one another, so that at a certain point in the microscope tube a magnified but inverted image of the object appears. This object is still further magnified by another lens in the eye-piece. When the rays of light reach the eye, the eye imagines that they have come in straight lines instead of being bent, and so the object appears much enlarged, as though it were near the object glass. In this picture the microscope is greatly simplified so that its principle may be easily understood. In modern instruments both the object glass and the glass of the eye-piece consist of several lenses, so arranged that they will rectify the distortion that is caused by the curvature of the glass.

THE DOOR THAT OPENS WITHOUT A TOUCH

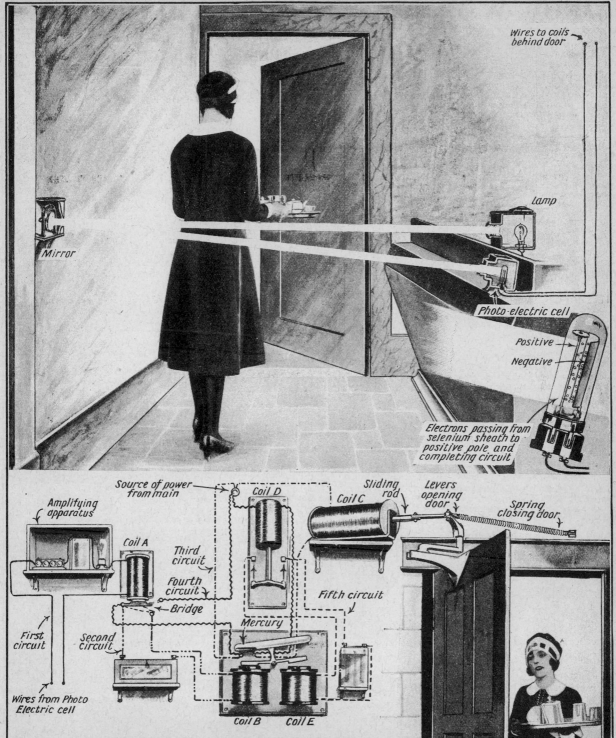

Wires to coils behind door

Lamp

Mirror

Photo-electric cell

Positive

Negative

Electrons passing from selenium sheath to positive pole and completing circuit

Amplifying apparatus

Source of power from main

Coil D

Coil C

Sliding rod

Levers opening door

Spring closing door

Coil A

Third circuit

Fourth circuit

Bridge

Fifth circuit

Mercury

First circuit

Second circuit

Wires from Photo Electric cell

Coil B

Coil E

Here we see the wonderful apparatus by means of which a waitress opens a door by approaching it. Light from a lamp is reflected back on a photo-electric cell, causing electrons of the metal selenium to pass to a positive rod, thereby completing an electric circuit. The current, amplified, energises a coil, A, making an iron rod into a magnet. This holds up a bridge of iron. When the waitress interrupts the beam of light the electrons no longer pass and the First Circuit is broken. The bridge drops from Coil A and completes the Second Circuit. Coil B is thereby energised and attracts one side of an iron bridge with a tube of mercury, which runs down and keeps the bridge tilted. The Third and Fourth Circuits are now completed. The Third Circuit energises Coil C, and an iron core, becoming a magnet, draws in a sliding rod, which works levers and opens the door. The Fourth Circuit energises Coil D, the iron core inside becoming a magnet and drawing up a rod with a bridge. When this reaches two studs the Fifth Circuit is completed, energising Coil E, which at once draws down the other end of the pivoted bridge, breaking the Third and Fourth Circuits, Coils C and D become de-energised and a spring closes the door once more. The rod drawn up by Coil D now falls and the Fifth Circuit is broken

HOW A TELESCOPE BRINGS THINGS NEAR

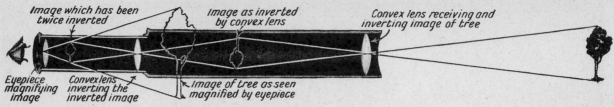

Image which has been twice inverted   *Image as inverted by convex lens*   *Convex lens receiving and inverting image of tree*

Eyepiece magnifying image   *Convex lens inverting the inverted image*   *Image of tree as seen magnified by eyepiece*

This picture-diagram shows an ordinary telescope for looking at objects on the Earth. It is known as a terrestrial telescope, from the Latin word terra, meaning the Earth. It differs from the astronomical telescopes shown below in producing images in their true position and not upside down. This result is brought about by using an extra convex lens. Rays of light pass from the object to be viewed to a convex lens known as the object glass, which corresponds to the object glass of a microscope as shown on page 110. This curved lens causes the rays to be bent at an angle, and to cross one another, forming an inverted image of the object at a certain point in the telescope tube. This inverted image is once more inverted by the convex lens first referred to, so that an image the right way up is formed near the eye-piece. The distant object seen is thus brought near to the eye and appears as if it is only a short distance away. In order that it may be seen better, it is viewed through a magnifying glass in the eye-piece, and so the object appears large as well as near.

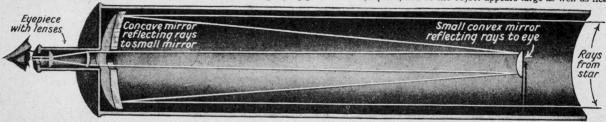

Eyepiece with lenses   *Concave mirror reflecting rays to small mirror*   *Small convex mirror reflecting rays to eye*   *Rays from star*

The earliest telescopes used by astronomers were like the terrestrial instrument shown above, except that there was no extra lens to show the object right way up. The largest astronomical telescopes, however, are of a different type known as reflecting telescopes, because the image of the star or other object is caught by a big mirror and reflected back to another mirror or prism. The type shown here is called the Cassegrainian telescope, after its French inventor Cassegrain, who lived in the 17th century. The rays from the star are caught by a large concave mirror near the eyepiece and reflected back to a small convex mirror at the other end of the telescope. This, in turn, reflects them back, through a small opening in the large mirror, to the eyepiece where the observer sees the star through lenses.

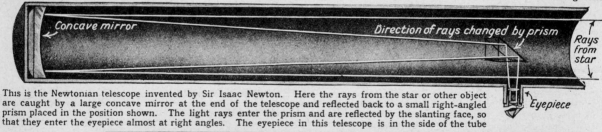

Concave mirror   *Direction of rays changed by prism*   *Rays from star*   *Eyepiece*

This is the Newtonian telescope invented by Sir Isaac Newton. Here the rays from the star or other object are caught by a large concave mirror at the end of the telescope and reflected back to a small right-angled prism placed in the position shown. The light rays enter the prism and are reflected by the slanting face, so that they enter the eyepiece almost at right angles. The eyepiece in this telescope is in the side of the tube.

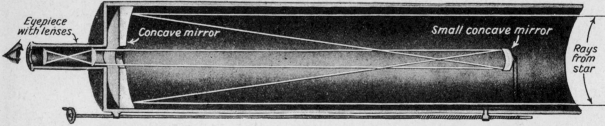

Eyepiece with lenses   *Concave mirror*   *Small concave mirror*   *Rays from star*

In this picture-diagram we have the oldest type of reflecting telescope invented by James Gregory, a Scottish mathematician, in 1663, and called after him the Gregorian telescope. Gregory was the actual inventor of the first reflecting telescope. It is very much like the Cassegrainian telescope shown above, except that the image is reflected from the large concave mirror to a small concave mirror instead of to a convex mirror. Then the rays are reflected back once more and pass through a small opening in the large mirror to the eyepiece.

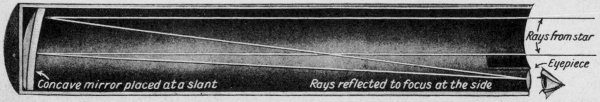

Rays from star   *Eyepiece*   *Concave mirror placed at a slant*   *Rays reflected to focus at the side*

Finally, we have here the Herschelian reflecting telescope invented by Sir William Herschel. In this instrument the concave mirror is slightly tipped so that the image of the star, instead of being formed in the centre of the tube, is formed near one side of it, and the observer thus looks directly towards the big mirror. It is the simplest type of reflecting telescope and involves the least loss of light, but the slant of the mirror causes some distortion of the image viewed, and for this reason the Herschelian type is now entirely abandoned.

THE PRISM THAT TELLS US WHAT THE SUN IS MADE OF

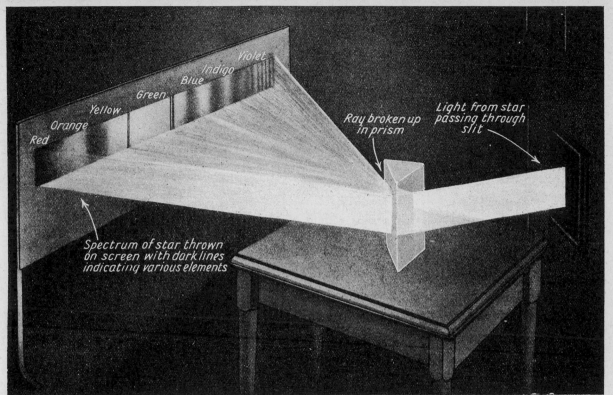

One of the greatest of all scientific discoveries took place when Sir Isaac Newton let sunshine into a dark room through a small hole and caused the light to fall on a prism. To his surprise, instead of getting a white image on a screen he saw a band of colour, and realised that sunlight was made up of seven colours. It was the beginning of the great science of spectroscopy, or the analysis of light by means of the spectroscope, an instrument containing a prism or series of prisms. Later it was found that the light from different elements produced lines on the band of colour always in the same relative positions and now, by means of the spectroscope, we can analyse the light of the sun or a star and tell what these bodies are made of. Helium was first found in the sun by the spectroscope

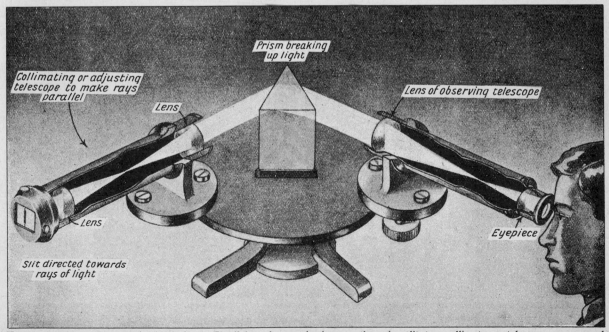

Here we see the spectroscope in simple form. The light to be examined comes through a slit, to a collimator or telescope, so arranged as to pass on a parallel pencil of rays to a prism. Here the light is broken up into its colours and falls on the object glass of another telescope through which the observer looks. An image of the spectrum forms at a focus in the telescope and the eyepiece magnifies it

Camera in
sound-proof booth

Microphone

Film reel
unexposed

Toothed
wheel

Shutter

Motor turning
toothed wheel

Film reel
exposed

Negative film of picture

Wires from generator

Loud speaker
behind screen

In these pages   we see how a talking picture is made and reproduced. Thousands of pictures of a scene, each a little different from the one before, are photographed on a film, the film being passed before the camera lens at a regular speed by electric machinery. At the same time the sounds of the scene are caught by a microphone, where the sound waves in the air vibrate a diaphragm and move a number of carbon granules through which an electric current is passing. This movement causes the current to fluctuate, and thus the sounds are transformed into a varying electric current. The current passes through an amplifier, where it is regulated to the necessary strength, and the wires are connected with a light gate in the sound-recording apparatus. The light gate consists of a slit through which a beam of light passes, and is focussed on to the edge of a film. The fluctuations of the current cause

REPRODUCED IN THE PICTURE HOUSE

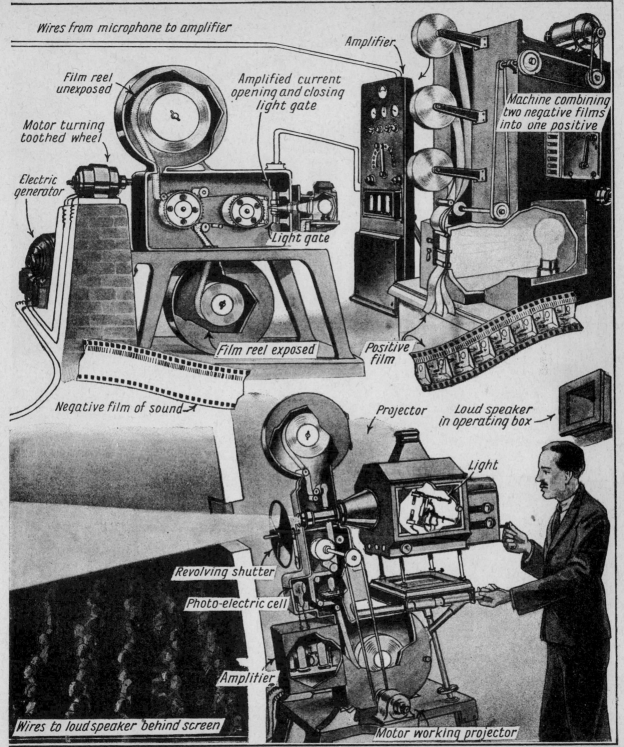

Wires from microphone to amplifier

Film reel unexposed

Amplified current opening and closing light gate

Amplifier

Machine combining two negative films into one positive

Motor turning toothed wheel

Electric generator

Light gate

Film reel exposed

Positive film

Negative film of sound

Projector

Loud speaker in operating box

Light

Revolving shutter

Photo-electric cell

Amplifier

Wires to loud speaker behind screen

Motor working projector

the slit to open and close in such a way as to vary the width through which the light passes. The result is the reproduction on the film of lines of varying density. From the two negative films a single positive film containing both picture and sound record is made. At the cinema the film is run through a projector, about ninety pictures passing before the lens each minute. Each picture is stationary for a moment, being cut off from others by a rapidly revolving shutter. The rapid succession of pictures thrown on the screen gives the illusion of continuous action. As the film runs through the projector a beam of light travels through the sound track on the edge of the film and is focussed on a photo-electric cell, which transforms the varying light intensities into electric fluctuations. These are amplified and carried by wires to loud speakers, where they are transformed into sound. The system shown is the Western Electric.

Elevator control
bar pulled back

Right
aileron

Aeroplane
rising

Wires to
elevator

Control wheel of
ailerons and
elevators

Wires to
rudder

Wires to
ailerons

Foot bar
control of
rudder

Pilot

Wires to
elevator

Right aileron
pulled up

Rudder pulled
to the right

Aileron control
wheel turned
to the right

Rudder
foot bar

Left aileron
pulled down

Aeroplane turning
to the right

In this double-page picture we see the way in which the airman controls his machine. The aeroplane shown is one of the latest machines of the ⸻ Airways. The pilot is able to turn his machine to the right or left or to rise or descend by moving the rudder and certain parts of the wings or tail of the machine. The parts of the wings that are moved are known as "ailerons," and the parts of the tail as "elevators." By operating the rudder and ailerons the aeroplane is made to turn about its longitudinal axis so that it tilts sideways, and the direction in which it turns depends upon whether the right aileron or left aileron is pulled up or down, and whether the rudder is turned to the right or left. As can be seen, these various parts of the machine are operated by a control wheel and foot-bar. The foot-bar moves the rudder and the control wheel the other parts. The wheel and foot-bar are connected by wires with the moving parts. When the airman wants to rise he raises the elevators on the tail of his machine, and the result is that the air, as it streams along the

Elevators pulled up

Elevator

Rudder

Elevator

Right aileron pulled down

Rudder pulled to the left

Aileron control wheel turned to the left

Rudder foot bar

Aeroplane turning to the left

Left aileron pulled up

Left aileron

back of the plane, rises over the elevators and pushes the tail of the machine down. This operation is shown in the small sketch at the top. When the airman wants to descend he lowers the elevators and the air underneath the aeroplane then pushes the tail up, so that the nose is inclined downwards. The method of turning is shown in the small pictures on the left and right. When the aeroplane is to be turned to the right, the pilot turns the control wheel to the right, and this pulls up the right aileron and lowers the left aileron. At the same time he presses on the foot-bar and turns the rudder to the right. The result of these motions is that the aeroplane tilts downwards on the right-hand side, because the air being pressed up by the raised right aileron pushes that side of the machine down. This motion, together with the turning of the rudder to the right, causes the aeroplane to move round to the right. The opposite is the case when the airman wishes to turn to the left. The right aileron is pulled down, the left aileron up, and the rudder turned to the left

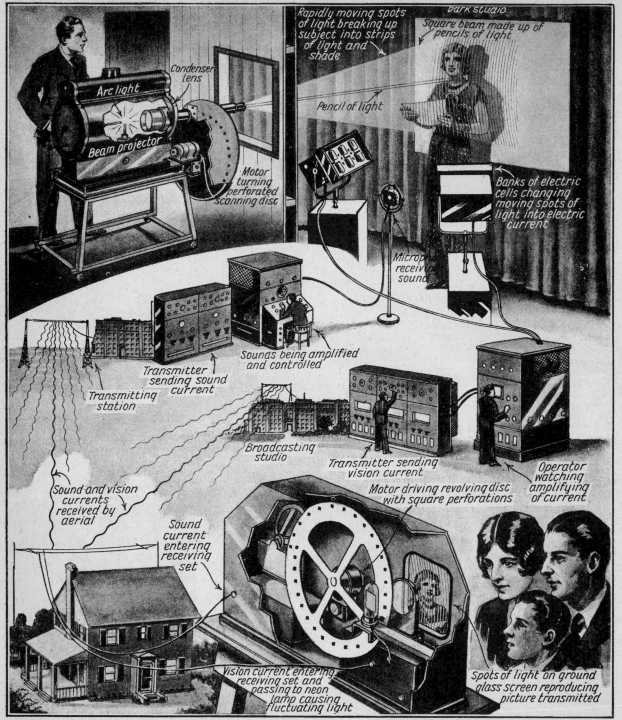

Rapidly moving spots of light breaking up subject into strips of light and shade

Dark studio

Square beam made up of pencils of light

Condenser lens

Arc light

Beam projector

Pencil of light

Motor turning perforated scanning disc

Banks of electric cells changing moving spots of light into electric current

Microphone receiving sound

Sounds being amplified and controlled

Transmitter sending sound current

Transmitting station

Broadcasting studio

Transmitter sending vision current

Operator watching amplifying of current

Motor driving revolving disc with square perforations

Sound and vision currents received by aerial

Sound current entering receiving set

Vision current entering receiving set and passing to neon lamp causing fluctuating light

Spots of light on ground glass screen reproducing picture transmitted

Television, invented by John Logie Baird, a Scotsman, seems almost more wonderful than ordinary sound wireless. In these pages we see how this wonder is performed. First of all, on the left-hand page we have the disc system. A person is singing in a darkened studio and a bright beam of light from an arc lamp shines upon her through a square opening. Between the light and the singer is revolving rapidly a disc perforated with thirty square holes arranged in spiral form. Each perforation passes before the beam of light and the rapid rotation causes the beam to be broken up into a series of pencils of light, which play all over the singer's form. If the disc rotated slowly a single spot of light would be seen playing over the subject, but by the rapid movement, 12½ revolutions a second, and the persistence of vision, the onlooker has the impression that the girl is standing in a continuous beam of light. Close to the girl are two banks of photo-electric cells which are exceedingly sensitive to every variation of light. As the pencil of light plays over the girl different amounts of light are reflected upon the cells, little light from the hair, for example, and much from the white teeth. These photo-electric cells change the light falling upon them into electricity and as the light fluctuates so the current fluctuates also. The current is very small but is amplified greatly, and being carefully controlled is sent by a transmitter from an aerial at the broadcasting station. Meanwhile, the sounds of the singing are broadcast in the ordinary way on another wave-length after being changed into electric current, amplified and controlled. After passing over hundreds of miles the electric waves transmitting the singer's form and movements are caught by the receiver's aerial and pass to a vision-receiving set. The electric current goes to a neon lamp with a plate which glows more or less according

WE SEE THINGS HAPPENING MILES AWAY

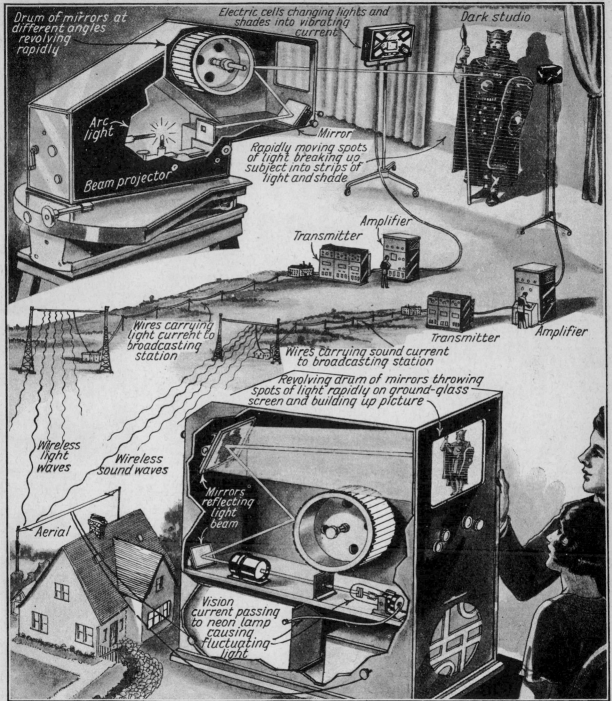

Drum of mirrors at different angles revolving rapidly

Electric cells changing lights and shades into vibrating current

Dark studio

Arc light

Beam projector

Mirror

Rapidly moving spots of light breaking up subject into strips of light and shade

Amplifier

Transmitter

Transmitter

Amplifier

Wires carrying light current to broadcasting station

Wires carrying sound current to broadcasting station

Revolving drum of mirrors throwing spots of light rapidly on ground-glass screen and building up picture

Wireless light waves

Wireless sound waves

Aerial

Mirrors reflecting light beam

Vision current passing to neon lamp causing fluctuating light

to the strength of current. Revolving in front of this lamp is a perforated disc moving at the same speed as the disc in the sending studio, and as the holes pass rapidly in front of the glowing plate the picture of the singer is built up in vertically moving spots of light and shade. Persistence of vision makes the many spots appear one picture. A big lens magnifies this image on a ground glass screen. The sound is received as in an ordinary wireless set. On the right-hand page is another method of television known as the drum method. The principle is similar, but instead of a perforated disc to break up the subject into spots of light and shade, a drum of thirty mirrors set at different angles breaks up the subject into thirty horizontal strips. From an arc light a square beam is focused on a mirror which deflects it on to the drum revolving very rapidly, and a thin spot of light traverses the singer or other object in horizontal strips. By their speed the light spots appear as streaks. The photo-electric cells change the fluctuating light into fluctuating current as before and the moving picture is transmitted across country. The electric waves are received by a lamp which glows according to the amount of current and this glow is directed through a powerful lens upon a mirror which deflects it to a revolving drum of mirrors like that at the transmitting station. The streaks of light into which the subject was broken up at the sending station are reproduced by the drum mirrors, and persistence of vision gives a complete picture as the streaks of light are thrown on a screen. On the next page still another method of television is explained, but it must be remembered that whatever the system the basic principle is the same, namely the breaking-up of the subject into points or lines of light which are transformed into electricity, sent across country, the electricity then being retransformed into points or lines of light to form the picture that is thrown on the screen of the receiving set for the observers to see

THE LATEST METHOD OF TELEVISION

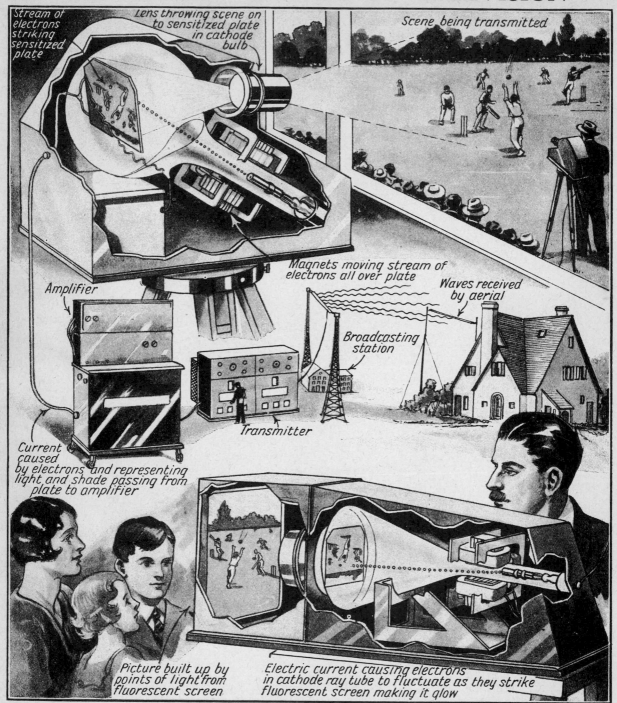

Stream of electrons striking sensitized plate

Lens throwing scene on to sensitized plate in cathode bulb

Scene being transmitted

Amplifier

Magnets moving stream of electrons all over plate

Waves received by aerial

Broadcasting station

Transmitter

Current caused by electrons and representing light and shade passing from plate to amplifier

Picture built up by points of light from fluorescent screen

Electric current causing electrons in cathode ray tube to fluctuate as they strike fluorescent screen making it glow

Here we see the most modern system of television known as the cathode ray system. A camera lens projects the scene to be transmitted upside down on to a sensitised plate suspended in a glass bulb. The plate is something like the retina of the eye, and is made up of millions of microscopic photo-electric cells in the form of globules of sensitive metal deposited on the surface. The bulb is a cathode ray tube, and this projects a narrow stream of electrons at the plate on which falls the scene to be transmitted. The stream of electrons, by means of electro-magnets surrounding the tube or bulb, is made to run to and fro over the plate very rapidly covering every part of it. Each minute photo-electric cell becomes electrically charged as the light from the scene strikes upon it, the charge varying with the amount of light. As the invisible stream of electrons strikes it each minute cell discharges its electricity, which is carried to an amplifier and broadcast from an aerial. There is thus a continual stream of fluctuating current representing the lights and shades of the picture being transmitted. The receiving set also has a cathode tube with a sensitised plate. The fluctuating current is led to the stream of electrons which also fluctuates in intensity and causes a sensitised plate to glow in varying degrees, the magnets keeping "in step" with those on the transmitter, that is making their movements correspond with those in the transmitter. The spots of light on the screen representing the lights and shades of the picture are formed so rapidly that the picture is built up, the eye seeing it as a whole, and not noticing that it consists of many spots. The observer looks at the picture through a magnifying lens which makes the picture big enough to see

Book 9

MANUAL of SIMPLIFIED EXPERIMENTS

EXPERIMENTS WITH MAGNETS & NEEDLES

THERE are many interesting experiments which we can carry out with a few needles and a couple of simple bar magnets. Some of these are given on this page, and no doubt others will suggest themselves.

A magnet, of course, has two poles, one of which we call the north pole and the other the south pole, although, of course, when

Two magnets with unlike poles together

Two magnets with like poles together

a magnet is suspended from the middle and comes to rest it is the end which points north which we call the north pole and that which points south the south pole. More accurate names would be the north-seeking and south-seeking poles. It is impossible to have a magnet which has a north pole at each end or a south pole at each end, or which has a pole at only one end the other end being neutral.

When we dip the end of a magnet into a box of iron filings we find that they adhere to that end, and if we dip the other end in we shall find that the filings will adhere to that end. The same thing happens if we lay the magnet in the box of filings. A great cluster will adhere to each end, but there will be none attaching themselves to the middle of the magnet.

If now we take two bar magnets and

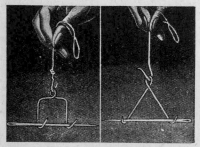

Two ways of suspending a magnetised needle

place them end to end we shall find that different things happen according to the way in which we place them. If, for example, as in the first picture we put the north pole of one magnet against the south pole of the other magnet no filings will adhere to where these two poles meet, although there will be plenty at the other

ends. The reason is that when the magnets are placed in this way the two bars really become one magnet.

But suppose we place the two magnets with like poles together, as in the second picture. Then they no longer form one magnet. They remain two magnets and the filings will adhere to the two north poles which are together.

Now let us suspend a sewing needle from one end of a bar magnet. Then over the top of the magnet run the second magnet, so that similar poles are over one another. The magnet will have been strengthened and the needle will still adhere. If, however, we reverse one of the magnets so that unlike poles are over one another the needle will drop away, for the south pole of one bar magnet will have neutralised the north pole of the other. Of course, it is assumed that both magnets are of the same size and strength.

We will now take one or two sewing needles and magnetise these by stroking each one in turn with the end of a bar magnet always in one direction and not to and fro. Very soon each needle becomes a magnet, as we can find by suspending it in some such way as shown in the pictures.

We make from thin wire a kind of stirrup in which the needle can rest. Either of the two forms shown will be satisfactory. If the needle in its holder now be suspended from a thread which is free to turn in any direction the needle will always come to

The strange behaviour of floating magnets

rest in one direction. It will point almost due north and south, the reason being that its ends point to the magnetic north and south poles which are not quite true north and south.

Now let us take a magnetised needle and suspend it by its middle. We hold it exactly over the centre of a bar magnet which has been laid north and south, and it hangs horizontally with its south pole pointing in the direction of the bar magnet's north pole and its north pole in the direction of the magnet's south pole.

If now we move the suspended needle magnet a little nearer one end we shall find that it will dip, that is, one end will be drawn down towards the pole of the bar magnet. If we move it the other way the opposite end will be drawn down, and if we take it to the end the needle will be drawn down so that it will stand vertically over the bar magnet's pole.

This tendency of the needle to move down slantingly is known as its "dip," and the needle of a compass always dips as it gets nearer either of the magnetic poles of the Earth. In the Latitude of London a free magnetic needle dips

at an angle of 67 degrees with the horizontal.

Now we can carry out a rather more elaborate experiment. After magnetising a number of sewing needles of equal length, we push them through small corks so as to make them float upright in a dish of water. In magnetising the needles we arrange that the eye end of each needle shall be the south pole and all the needles are made to float with the points downwards.

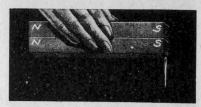

How two bar magnets strengthen one another

How two bar magnets neutralise one another

When the corks with the magnetised needles are placed together in the centre of the vessel they begin to float apart towards the sides. The reason is that like poles being close together repel one another and each helps to drive its neighbours away.

If now we take a bar magnet and hold its north pole in the middle of the vessel we shall find that the magnets arrange themselves in a certain way. Their south poles want to repel one another, but the north pole of the bar magnet attracts them and so, torn between two forces, they move till a state of equilibrium is brought about.

If there is an odd number of needles one will be attracted to the north pole of the bar magnet and others will arrange themselves round in the form of a ring.

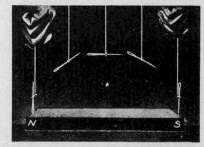

How a magnetised needle dips over a magnet

If the number be different the way in which they arrange themselves will be different, and it is interesting to experiment with a set of magnetised needles floating in the vessel and varying in number from four to twenty-four. The pattern that the floating corks form will be different in each case.

SCIENCE EXPERIMENTS FOR EVERYBODY

MANY experiments can be performed in the home with ordinary materials and utensils that are found there. Here, for instance, is one illustrating

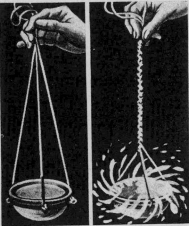

An illustration of centrifugal force

we shall not spill any water or oil. Holding the tubes closely we now sway them gently, and soon we see the two liquids changing places. The water being heavier is drawn down by gravitation and the paraffin rises into the top tube.

Take a glass of lemonade in which is a lemon pip, and with a straw suck up the lemonade. As we withdraw air from the straw the pressure of air on the liquid in the glass drives it up the tube. Now place the end of the straw against the lemon pip. When we draw, no lemonade comes. The end being closed the lemonade cannot enter, and so the straw is pressed together by the pressure of the outside air.

A somewhat similar experiment is to take a tumbler and warm it and then stand it on a piece of shiny cloth. As the rarefied air in the tumbler cools, a partial vacuum is caused and the pressure of the outside air drives the cloth up into the tumbler.

To illustrate capillarity place a square of cloth, such as a dishcloth on the surface of the water in a bowl. It floats for some time, but soon capillary attraction causes water to enter the openings of the cloth.

It becomes wet, and then being heavier sinks by gravitation.

Here is a centre of gravity experiment. Make a cylinder of thin cardboard and

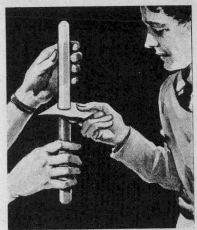

Water that sinks and oil that rises

centrifugal force. We take a round tin bowl and support it by three strings, as shown in the first picture. We fill the bowl with water to the brim, and then carefully twist it round and round till the string is wound up into one cord. Then we allow the string to unwind rapidly. As the bowl turns round water is thrown off at a tangent from every point, this being due to centrifugal force which causes a moving object to go on in a straight line unless something stops it.

The following experiment illustrates gravitation. We take two test tubes, filling one to the brim with paraffin slightly coloured with iodine and the other with water coloured with washing blue. We place a piece of thin cardboard over the test tube of water, pressing it close, and then we turn the tube upside down. We now put it inverted exactly over the mouth of the test tube of oil and get someone to pull away the card gently. If we are careful

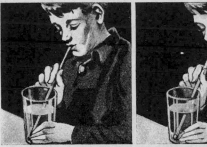

Two illustrations of the results of suction

A floating cloth gets wet by capillary attraction and sinks

paint it to look like a man. Paste paper over the top to round it off, and do the same at the bottom, but here place a rounded piece of lead or make a little compartment and fill it with shot. The little man will not now lie down. When you press him down he at once pops up. The shot or lead places the centre of gravity very low, and so the figure stands upright to be in a position of stable equilibrium.

We must be careful in making this amusing little toy to see that the lump of lead or little pocket containing the shot is secured by seccotine or glue to the bottom end of the tube, otherwise the figure will not rise promptly every time we lay it down, because the weight that keeps the centre of gravity low will shift about.

A number of these little gravity toys can be made, each representing a different figure, or a set of them can be made all alike and painted to look like soldiers.

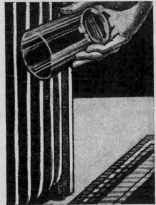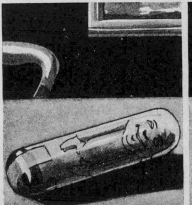

On the left is an experiment showing air pressure. A glass warmed at the fire or radiator is placed over cloth and when the air cools the cloth rises up into the glass. On the right is a simple centre of gravity toy which anyone can make

THE SCIENCE OF A LIGHTED CANDLE

THE wonders of modern science which seem so astonishing to-day are all the result of experiment. For centuries men have been testing and proving things, and one experiment has led to another, until marvellous discoveries have been made which can be put to practical use in industry and everyday life.

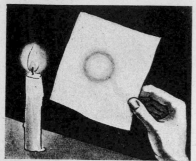
The circular flame of a candle

A little experiment is worth a great deal of book knowledge, and every boy and girl can become a practical scientist in the sense that he or she can perform scientific experiments.

To do this it is not necessary to have elaborate apparatus and expensive chemicals.

Take, for example, such a familiar object as a candle. Here are a number of experiments which we can perform and which will teach us a good deal of science. It seems a very ordinary thing to light a candle, and the flame does not appear very interesting. But as a matter of fact the flame is well worth studying, as Michael Faraday, the great scientist, discovered long ago.

Though the candle is burning the whole of the flame itself is not alight.

Water collected from a burning candle

You can prove this by holding a sheet of white notepaper for a moment or two horizontally in the lower part of the flame near the wick. When you remove the paper you will find, as in the first picture on this page, that there is a black, sooty ring, and outside this a ring where the paper is

scorched. Why is this? Well, the scorched ring is caused by the burning of the vapour of the flame, and the sooty ring consists of lamp-black from the particles of carbon in the bright section of the flame. But inside the black ring the paper is left white, because there the vapour rising from the burning candle remains unburnt.

The candle-flame, if you look carefully, will be seen to consist of three parts, a faint outside part, where the vapour is burning, a luminous section inside this, which consists of incandescent particles of carbon, and then a

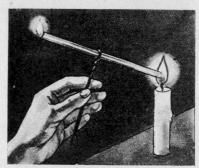
Collecting gas from a candle flame

faint bluish section right inside, which consists of unburnt combustible vapour from the fat of the candle.

If you hold a piece of thin glass tubing with one end in the faint blue of the flame, you can draw off this vapour and light it at the other end of the tube, where it burns with a faint

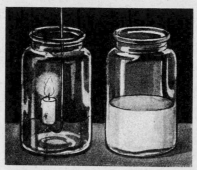
Carbon dioxide produced by a candle flame

light. Hold the glass tube with a piece of bent iron.

It is easy to put out a candle by blowing it, but you can also extinguish the flame by cooling it without blowing it. Take a piece of copper wire, such as you can buy at the ironmonger's, make a spiral, and then lower it while it is quite cold over the flame, which will go out, because the wire absorbs the heat. If, however, you heat the wire beforehand and repeat the experiment, the flame will go on burning.

When a candle is alight hydrogen gas is burning, but a certain amount

of hydrogen gas escapes without burning. You can prove this by holding a tumbler over the flame. Little drops of water will form, and finally trickle off the tumbler. These are due to the hydrogen gas combining with the oxygen of the air. Water, as we know, is made up of oxygen and hydrogen gases.

If you burn a candle in a jam jar,

A novel way of putting out a candle

covering the jar over so that no fresh air can get in, the flame will soon go out. The carbon of the candle-fat, when burning, combines with the oxygen of the air, forming carbon dioxide gas, and this gas will not support combustion. You can prove the gas is in the jar by removing the candle and pouring in some clear lime water. The carbon dioxide will change the lime in the lime water into chalk, making the liquid milky, and gradually the particles of chalk will sink to the bottom of the jar.

That a candle uses up air when burning can be very simply proved. Stand two lengths of candle in a bowl, fixing them to a piece of wood if necessary. Pour in water, light the candles, and invert over them a glass jam jar, seeing that its edges are below the water.

Showing that a burning candle uses up air

Soon the candles will go out, and when the jar becomes cool the water will rise in it. The candles in burning have used up some of the oxygen of the air, and the water rises to take its place. About one-fifth of the vacant space of the jar will be occupied by the risen water.

EXPERIMENTS IN THE SCIENCE OF BALANCE

THERE are many simple experiments which can be carried out at home to illustrate the science of balance, and some of these are quite interesting as games and tricks.

To balance a dinner plate on a needle's point seems a difficult task, but when it

each blade going under the point of another blade and over the third.

A good balancing game for a party is that of lighting one candle from another while sitting on a bottle with the feet crossed. The tendency of the bottle to roll about and the unstable

feet and we have to pick up the match-box without moving our feet. When we bend forward our centre of gravity is brought forward and we cannot put back the lower part of our body to counteract this. We therefore fall forward.

There is a way, however, of doing

On the left we see how to balance a dinner plate on the point of a needle, and on the right how to support a basin on the blades of three knives, the handles of which rest on three tumblers. The middle picture shows a difficult feat, that of lighting one candle from another while we sit on a bottle with our feet crossed. Paper should be spread to catch falling grease

is done in the manner shown in the first picture it is easy. At equal distances we paste on the plate four half corks, the corks being split down their length. These are so fixed that part projects over the plate. Then we stick into the corks the teeth of four forks as shown. A needle is stuck into the cork of a bottle, and the plate can now, with a little care, be balanced quite well on the point of the needle. The four forks

equilibrium of the sitter make it very difficult to keep steady enough to light the second candle. To avoid grease falling on the clothes or the floor it is well to spread newspapers.

Here is another balancing trick which gives a good deal of amusement at a party. We ask someone to stand against the wall, his foot flush against the skirting-board, his shoulder and his head also touching the wall. In this

this. Keeping our feet still, we turn our bodies to the left or right and stoop that way to pick up the matchbox.

It must always be remembered that if a body is to remain still a vertical line from the centre of gravity downwards must fall within the base on which the body stands. Anything therefore like the bending forward while against the wall upsets this arrangement, and our bodies are thrown forward so that we

The boy on the left is asked to raise the outside leg, as shown in the second picture, without coming away from the wall. But although it looks easy it is quite an impossible thing to do. On the right we see two ways of attempting to pick up a matchbox at our feet while our feet are flush against the wall. The first method is impossible, but the second is quite possible

have brought the centre of gravity of the combined plate and forks very low.

Another interesting balancing feat of a different kind is shown in another picture. Here we balance a basin or carafe of water on the blades of three knives, the handles of the knives resting on three tumblers. This is done by interlacing the blades of the knives,

position he is asked to raise the outside leg. Of course, directly he does so his centre of gravity is changed, and he comes away from the wall.

A somewhat similar balancing experiment is shown in the last pictures. We stand with our back to the wall, our heels, shoulders and head all touching it. Then a matchbox is placed at our

put out our foot or hands to prevent ourselves from falling.

In the ordinary way, if we stoop to pick anything up as we bend forward the upper part of our body, we press the other part of the body in the opposite direction, and this preserves the balance with the centre of gravity in the right position to prevent overturning.

EXPERIMENTS WITH SIMPLE CHEMICALS

WE can all perform chemical experiments without going to a laboratory and having expensive apparatus. Nor do we need to get together a collection of elaborate chemicals such as are found in a school or college. There are plenty of chemicals in the home, and with very little apparatus indeed we can carry out some interesting experiments.

For example, take a rusty nail or other iron object that has been lying

Separating iron filings from red rust

outside and scrape the red rust into a plate with an old knife. Then take some iron filings, such as we can ourselves file from a nail or screw. Mix the two substances together, and then try to separate them.

How will you do this? Well, there is a very simple way. Hold a magnet over the mixture, and at once the iron filings will adhere to the ends of the magnet, but the red rust will be left behind in the plate.

The magnet attracts the iron filings, but it does not attract the rust, for the simple reason that the rust, which is iron oxide, is a different substance with different qualities, although it contains iron. The oxygen of the air, which is a chemical element, combined with the iron of the nail, which is also

Testing acids and alkalies with litmus

an element, to form oxide of iron which is a chemical compound and has qualities different from the elements.

Another interesting experiment can be carried out with red and blue litmus paper, of which we can obtain a few strips for a penny at the chemist's. We place in a number of

egg-cups or saucers various liquids, such, for example, as soda water, lemonade, liquid ammonia, salt water, and vinegar. We want to discover which of these are acids and which are alkalies and which are neutral salts.

Ammonia from soda and sal-ammoniac

We do this by testing them with the strips of litmus paper. The acids will turn blue litmus red, the alkalies will turn red litmus blue, and the neutral liquids will have no effect on either.

Here is another interesting experiment. We take a little sal-ammoniac and crush it into small fragments. Then we place it in an egg-cup or saucer with some crushed or powdered washing soda. When we mix the two together we shall find that if we put our noses near the mixture that ammonia gas is being given off. The elements of which the two substances are combined re-arrange themselves

Hydrogen from iron filings and acetic acid

into new combinations and ammonia gas is formed, while common salt and water are left behind.

We can make hydrogen gas in a test tube by putting inside a few iron filings, and then pouring over them a little

acetic acid. Vinegar is really acetic acid, but the acetic acid we get at the chemist's is stronger. We can light the hydrogen with a match at the mouth of the tube as it is escaping.

Here is an experiment which we can carry out with a little soap, soda and water. We dissolve some ordinary yellow soap, say, half an ounce, in two cupfuls of distilled water—freshly collected rain water will do. The soap needs to be flaked, stirred up in the

Making hard water with salt

water, and the whole heated gently without bringing it to the boil.

When we have the solution, we drop in a couple of tablespoonfuls of ordinary cooking salt well ground up by means of a rolling pin. This salt will dissolve in the water and at once flakes will be seen floating. The explanation is that the water, owing to the salt dissolved in it, has become hard, and hard water will never hold soap in solution properly.

To prove that some substances will not burn, that is will not combine with oxygen, we can carry out this experiment. Soak a piece of white cotton in brine several times, so that there may be a good coating of salt. Now with the cotton tie up a light ring and suspend it from a metal rod. At

The cord that will not burn

the same time suspend another ring with unsoaked cotton.

Set light to both the threads and we shall find that while the ring suspended from the untreated cotton falls, the other one remains suspended because the coating of salt does not burn.

SOME SIMPLE ELECTRICAL EXPERIMENTS

THERE are many simple electrical experiments which we can perform at home. For instance, on a dry day, when our hair is perfectly dry, if we comb it rapidly with a vulcanite comb we shall probably see a number of electric sparks and hear their crack. In the same way, if we

Rubbed amber generates electricity

Glass rubbed with a silk cloth produces electricity. A clay pipe balanced on the edge of a tumbler can be made to move by bringing near the stem another tumbler electrified by rubbing with silk. It will follow the glass. A sheet of glass supported on books and rubbed with a silk handkerchief will

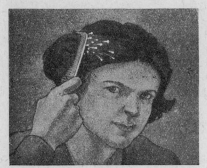
Electric sparks obtained by combing the hair with a vulcanite comb

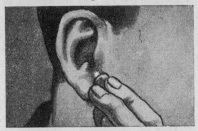
An electrified amber bead will, if held to the ear, cause a spark

A vulcanite comb rubbed on the sleeve becomes electrified and attracts paper

Stroking a cat's fur produces electricity

A paper cross can be made to rotate by electrifying a tumbler by rubbing

A sheet of glass rubbed with silk will make little paper figures underneath dance

Sealing-wax rubbed with flannel becomes electrified and raises the hair

Brown paper can be electrified by rubbing with the sleeve

An electrified tumbler will attract a balanced pipe

stroke the cat's back rapidly we shall see and hear sparks.

We can generate electricity by rubbing a number of substances. Sealing-wax, for example, if rubbed with flannel, becomes electrified, and if held above our hair will attract it. Similarly a vulcanite comb when rubbed will attract little pieces of paper. It was by rubbing amber that the Ancient Greeks first discovered electricity, and the name "electricity" comes from the Greek word for amber. We can generate electricity by rubbing an amber bead and get a spark by holding it to our ear.

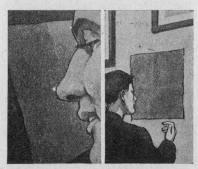
The electrified paper held to the nose causes a spark, and the paper can also be attached to the wall without support

make little paper puppets placed underneath dance up and down. A cross cut out of stiff paper and balanced on the point of a needle stuck in a cork may be made to move mysteriously if a warmed tumbler be placed over it and the glass rubbed outside with silk. By cutting a point on one arm of the cross we can make this turn in any direction by rubbing the glass at that side. We can get an electric spark by rubbing a sheet of brown paper with our sleeve and then holding it to our nose. The electrified paper will also stick to the wall without falling.

EXPERIMENTS WITH FAMILIAR SUBSTANCES

WE often read of chemists making tests to find out whether or not substances contain certain chemicals. Well, we can make such chemical tests ourselves.

For example, we can always detect starch by means of the iodine test. Mix a little ordinary household starch with water to make it liquid. Now into it pour one drop of iodine, a chemical that is kept in most homes to put on cuts as an antiseptic.

The starch where the iodine falls turns, not brown, but a purplish-blue or black. Iodine is thus a test for starch. We can tell what foods have starch in them by testing them with iodine. If they turn black, blue or purple they have starch, and if they do not turn any of these colours, then we may be sure they have no starch in them.

Try the iodine test on a cut potato, cornflour, powdered sugar, tapioca, custard powder, an onion, salt, milk, and other substances in the larder and see which contain starch.

Here is another pair of experiments that prove that sugar is a chemical compound and not a mere mixture. It is made up of carbon and the two gases of which water is composed, namely oxygen and hydrogen.

Sugar on the Shovel

Put a little sugar on a shovel and hold it over the fire or a gas-ring. What happens? The sugar melts and gives off water vapour and after a time nothing but a mass of black carbon is left. Now take a little powdered carbon and mix it up with some water in a tumbler. Nothing happens, no matter how well we mix the substances. Here are the three elements that form sugar—carbon, oxygen and hydrogen—yet we cannot produce sugar by mixing them. The explanation is that mere mixing will not do, the three elements must

form a chemical combination before they become sugar.

Take a glass of home-made lemonade made from lemons. Now stir up in it half a teaspoonful of carbonate of soda such as is used by the cook in making

Trying the iodine test on starch and on a freshly cut potato

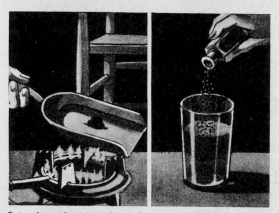
Sugar burnt becomes charcoal, water being driven off, but charcoal and water mixed will not make sugar

cakes. What happens? There is a fizzing sound and bubbles begin to rise in the lemonade. It is effervescing or bubbling up. The carbon in the soda combines with some of the

oxygen in the water forming carbon dioxide gas and it is this gas escaping which causes the bubbles and the fizzing.

Something of the same kind happens when the cook puts the soda in the cake or the baker puts yeast in the dough. Carbon dioxide gas is formed and the bubbles make little holes in the dough, which results in the cake or loaf being light when cooked instead of being heavy and stodgy. The dough rises as the cook says, that is, it swells, because it is blown out by the many little bubbles of gas.

Making Hydrogen Gas

We can make hydrogen gas in a very simple way if we have a test-tube and a little granulated zinc. Probably we can get these at the chemist's for a few if we have none. We put the zinc in the bottom of the test-tube and pour on it a little diluted spirits of salts. In a moment or two a gas is given off, which is hydrogen and we can prove that it is inflammable, that is that it burns, by holding a lighted match at the mouth of the tube. The hydrogen which is being given off catches light and burns with a faint blue flame, which is very hot. The test tube, during the course of the experiment, must be held with a piece of wire bent into a holder. Spirits of salts are kept in most houses for cleaning purposes and very little is needed for this experiment. Be sure to dilute it with water before pouring on the zinc.

One more experiment illustrates chemical action. Take a fragment of some delicate coloured material and put it in a saucer or basin. Then pour on it some liquid ammonia and leave it for a time. After a period, we shall find that the colour has almost disappeared. This is due to the chemical action of the ammonia upon the dyes.

On the left we see how soda placed in lemonade forms carbon dioxide gas, which escapes, causing a fizzing. Next we see how hydrogen gas may be made in a tube from zinc and diluted spirits of salts. It burns with a light blue but very hot flame if lighted with a match. On the right we see how ammonia takes the colour out of a coloured fabric

SOME SIMPLE EXPERIMENTS WITH AIR

There are many simple experiments which we can perform to show the supporting power of the air, the force of compressed air and the movements of gases.

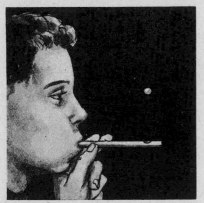
Keeping a pellet suspended in the air

We take a small metal tube closed at one end, such as a metallic penholder, and not far from the closed extremity drill a small hole. Then we take a small piece of bread and knead it perfectly round. Next, we lay it on the small hole and blow through the tube and the column of air passing out of the hole will lift the bread pellet and support it as long

A paper bag full of compressed air

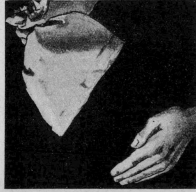
About to burst the bag of compressed air

as we continue blowing and keep the tube perfectly horizontal.

A similar experiment can be carried out with a pea and a small tube of any kind. Holding the tube upright, we rest the pea on the opening at the end, and then blow up the tube. The pea rises and is maintained as we blow.

Even the bursting of a blown-out paper bag is an interesting experiment, which will teach us a good deal of science. We blow the bag out only slightly, and it is difficult to burst it with a bang of the hand and even if it does burst, there is little noise.

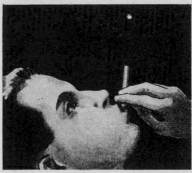
A pea supported in the air

But if we continue blowing into the bag after it is swelled out, we are compressing the air inside, and then the bursting of the bag is accompanied by a loud report. This is due to the compressed air escaping violently and setting up waves in the air.

We can tell how real a substance the air is by pressing our fingers against the bag when it is blown out.

The deflection of the air is shown

Extinguishing a candle behind a bottle

in the following experiment. Put a lighted candle on a table and in front of it a round bottle of the usual shape, such as a vinegar bottle. Now blow hard on the bottle. At once the candle is extinguished, the current of air having been deflected round the sides of the bottle so as to converge on the candle flame at the back.

Here is an experiment in which we form a sort of miniature Magdeburg Sphere. Take two similar tumblers. Light a piece of candle and place it

in one tumbler, and then put on the tumbler a piece of stout paper saturated with water. Now fit the other tumbler exactly on top. The heat of the flame rarefies the air in the bottom tumbler

Miniature Magdeburg Hemispheres

and the outside pressure of the air holds the tumblers closely together so that the bottom one can be raised by lifting the upper one.

Take an empty bottle and blow into it for some time. This fills it with compressed air, and if we close the neck and then release our hand when the mouth is near a candle flame, the flame will be blown out.

The bottle containing compressed air

Blowing out a candle with compressed air

129

CENTRE OF GRAVITY EXPERIMENTS

THERE are many interesting experiments which we can carry out to illustrate the principle of the centre of gravity, and some of these are illustrated on this page. In the

How to stand ready for the stool experiment

Having lifted the stool we find it impossible to rise to an erect position

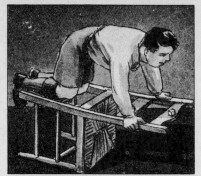

How the chair and sugar are placed

When we try to seize the sugar with our lips we shall overbalance unless very careful

makes it impossible to reach the erect position.

In the second experiment we place a strong kitchen chair on the ground in the position shown, with a piece of lump sugar on the upper rail. Now, kneeling on the lower bar of the chair and grasping the side rails, we bend forward and take up the sugar with our lips. The result will probably be as shown in the second of the two pictures. The centre of gravity being displaced causes us to overbalance. But by keeping the rear of our body well back and crouching low the sugar can be taken up without overbalancing.

For the third experiment we need a pencil and a ring. One experimenter holds the pencil and the other has to try to place the ring over its point. Before making the attempt, however,

How to stand ready for the pole experiment

With the back to the wall it is easy to pass under the pole and regain our position

first experiment we place a fairly heavy stool close against the wall and then take up our position facing it with our feet on the ground just twice as far from the wall as the width of the stool.

Now, bending forward with our legs quite straight to the hips and our head resting against the wall, as shown in the first picture, we grasp the stool and raise it as in the second picture. What we have to do now, while holding the stool, to try to raise ourselves to the erect position without moving our feet or legs. The displacement of the centre of gravity of our body now that we are holding the stool

The experimenters each on one knee try to put the ring over the pencil without overbalancing

each player has to hold up one of his or her feet with the hand as shown. This necessitates the performer resting on one knee only, and naturally it is very difficult to keep upright, as each player is in a state of unstable equilibrium like a pegtop balanced on its peg.

In the final experiment we need a broomstick or other pole, such as that which a boy scout carries. The experiment is to rest one end in the angle made by the floor and the wall, and then to pass the whole of the body underneath it without moving the end of the pole and without overbalancing. With our backs to the wall it will not be an impossible feat.

SIMPLE EXPERIMENTS CARRIED OUT WITH WATER

HERE are some interesting experiments which can be carried out with water. We all know the principle of the diving bell. If we fill a glass bowl nearly full of water and then invert a tumbler in it, we shall see that the level of the water in the tumbler is lower than that of the water outside. This is due to the presence of the air in the tumbler. Knowing this, we can perform an interesting experiment The problem is to

looks like the smoke and flame from a volcano. The spirit rises because it is of less specific gravity than the water.

We can make a miniature steamboat by using two empty eggshells and forming a model of a boat from cardboard. The seams must be caulked with sealing-wax to make the boat water-tight. Pins and black thread will represent the bulwarks, and at the stern we fix a rudder working on a pin. Two pieces of iron wire bent

eyes on the shell, and with red flannel make a little bag in the form of a fish's body. Ballast the shell with shot, so that it will keep upright in water, and insert the blown egg as shown in the picture, the hole being innermost. Stick the bag to the shell with sealing-wax. Now place it in a jar of water, closed with a piece of india-rubber tied tightly over the mouth. By pressing on the rubber the fish can be made to rise or sink at pleasure. The

On the left sugar remains dry under water ; in the centre a miniature volcano, and on the right a model steamboat with egg-shell boiler

place a lump of sugar under water without wetting it.

We put the sugar on a cork taken from a pickle jar, and let this float on the water. Then we invert a glass over it. We shall see the sugar supported by the cork floating inside the glass at a much lower level than the water in the bowl. When we withdraw the glass the sugar will be dry.

An interesting experiment is to make a miniature volcano in a glass bowl. We

and each resting in a small notch in the side of the boat form a bed for one of the blown eggshells, which has a little hole in the small end. Water has to be inserted so that when the egg is horizontal the water is almost up to the level of the hole. This is the boiler.

We place it on the bent wires with the hole pointing to the stern, a little above the level of the bulwarks. For furnace we place underneath the boiler half an egg-shell standing in the centre of a pickle

ballast must be adjusted for the fish to remain normally at the surface. The pressure of the hand forces a small portion of water into the shell, rendering it heavier, and so it sinks.

You can swing a glass of water round rapidly without spilling any, the power of centrifugal force overcoming the force of gravity, and stopping the water falling.

Next take a jar which has a tightly-fitting cork, and bore through the cork a

On the left a moving fish made from an eggshell ; in the centre a centrifugal force experiment, and on the right the magic moving balls

place at the bottom of the bowl a little bottle containing methylated spirits coloured red. We cork the bottle, but bore a very small hole through the cork perpendicularly from top to bottom Then with clay or plaster of Paris we mould a miniature mountain covering the bottle and in the apex make a small opening The glass bowl is nearly filled with water If we agitate the water a little we shall suddenly see rising from the crater of the clay mountain a stream of red spirit which

bottle cork, scooped out to form a ring, and secured to the boat by wax. In this half eggshell a little wadding is placed. On it we pour methylated spirits, and then set it alight, having first placed our boat in a bath of water. After a few seconds the water will boil, steam will rush out of the hole in the end of the boiler, and the reaction will drive the boat forward.

Here is another experiment with an egg. Blow the eggshell by making one hole and sucking the contents out. Then draw two

hole big enough for the neck of a funnel. Insert the funnel and seal up the connection to make the joint air-tight. Now half fill the jar with water, drop into it the matter from the blue and white packets of a Seidlitz powder. Quickly cork up the bottle and place in the funnel two or three balls of cork. The bicarbonate of soda and the tartaric acid of the packets acted upon by the water combine, and carbon dioxide gas is released. As it escapes it keeps tossing up the corks.

A GROUP OF SIMPLE OPTICAL EXPERIMENTS

The tiger that enters the cage when looked at as shown here

How to make the bird on one side enter the cage on the other

Here is another experiment which shows clearly that light is bent when it passes from one medium into another, as from air into water or from water into air. Take a card and cut two slits in it. Let the Sun's rays pass through these slits and shine upon a dark tablecloth. We shall see two bars of light. Now, keeping the card in position, hold a glass of water under one of the slits. At once the position of the bar of light on the cloth will change, because the ray of light has been bent by the water.

An amusing Pepper's ghost toy

HERE are some interesting experiments that help us to understand things about light and seeing. Draw on a post card a cage and about half an inch away a tiger. Then, holding the card in one hand, take another post card in the other hand and hold this at right angles between the cage and the tiger. Bring the face close to the card, so that the left eye sees the cage only and the other eye the tiger only. After looking for a few seconds the tiger will seem to move forward and enter the cage. This is due to the separate impressions received by the two eyes being combined by the seeing part of the brain.

We can obtain a good optical illusion of the Pepper's ghost type in the following way. Take a wooden box and make a round opening in one side. Place a glass of water in what, in the picture, is the farthest corner, and fix diagonally across the box a sheet of plain glass. On the near side of this stand a small piece of candle. Light it, and if the top of the box is open cover it with a piece of wood. Now look through the opening, and the candle will seem to be burning inside the

tumbler of water. The tumbler is seen through the glass at the same place that the candle is reflected upon the glass. Before showing the experiment to anyone else we must be sure to get the candle and glass in the right positions.

In the bottom picture on this page we have an optical illusion. Let us see which of the three figures we think is the tallest, and then measure. We may be surprised to find that all three are the same height. The lines drawn in perspective give us a wrong impression. The third figure appears far away from the first, and we naturally think it must be very much bigger.

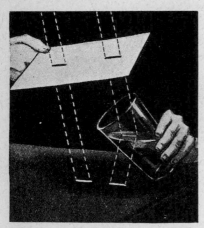

A simple experiment to prove that light rays are bent when they are passing from air to water

Another interesting experiment with a cage can be performed in this way. Take a small card about two inches deep and three inches wide, and on one side draw a bird-cage, and on the other side, but the reverse way, that is, upside down, a bird. Now fasten a piece of thin twine to each side of the card and begin twisting the threads backwards and forwards, so that the card rotates to and fro rapidly. The bird will appear inside the cage. This is owing to the persistence of vision, the images of the cage and the bird remaining on the retina so that one combines with the other.

Which is the tallest of these three figures? When you have guessed measure them

Shadows of Napoleon and Louis XVI cast by carved wooden blocks that disguise their object

Some interesting experiments can be made with a penknife and some pieces of wood by carving the wood in such a way as to throw shadows upon the wall representing faces. The last picture gives some examples of these. In troubled political times in France people often carried a piece of carved wood which would throw a shadow of their favourite sovereign upon the wall when held near a light.

Sometimes the treasonable toy was small enough to go in the pocket, while at other times the carving was on the handle of a walking-stick carried in the hand.

Book 10

BEHIND *the* SCENES *of*
GREAT INVENTIONS

A WONDERFUL AGRICULTURAL MACHINE

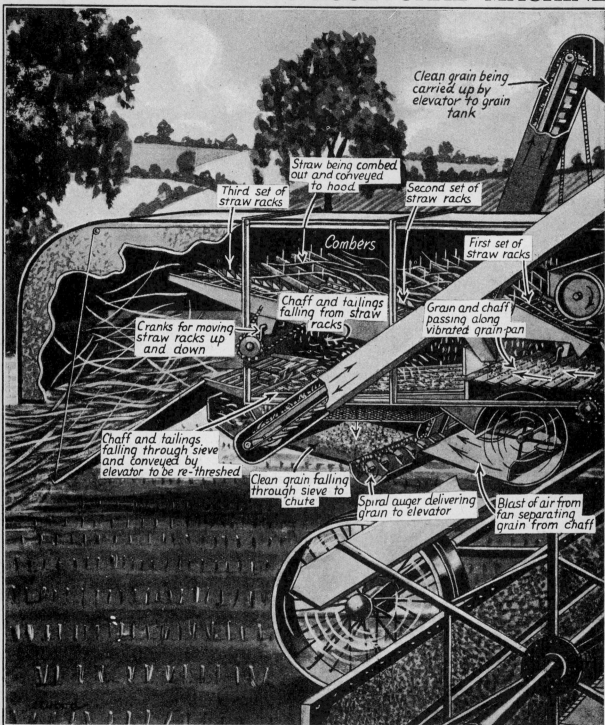

Clean grain being carried up by elevator to grain tank

Straw being combed out and conveyed to hood

Third set of straw racks

Second set of straw racks

Combers

First set of straw racks

Cranks for moving straw racks up and down

Chaff and tailings falling from straw racks

Grain and chaff passing along vibrated grain pan

Chaff and tailings falling through sieve and conveyed by elevator to be re-threshed

Clean grain falling through sieve to chute

Spiral auger delivering grain to elevator

Blast of air from fan separating grain from chaff

In this picture we see how one of the most remarkable of all agricultural machines cuts the corn as it moves along, threshes it, separates the grain from the chaff and stores it in a tank, passing the straw along to the rear of the machine. This wonderful and efficient machine is known as the McCormick-Deering Harvester-Thresher. It is drawn by a tractor which also supplies the power to work the machine. As the machine travels, revolving arms pull the growing grain towards a platform, while cutters cut it off three inches from the ground. The cut stalks fall upon the platform and are carried by a canvas conveyor and elevator to a feeder-conveyor. This takes them to a spiked cylinder where, as they pass between the cylinder and concave shapes underneath, the grain is threshed out and falls upon a grain pan. This is vibrated so that the threshed grain passes across it until it reaches the end, when a blast of air from a fan blows away the chaff and other refuse known as tailings, and the clean grain falls through a sieve on to a chute and runs down into a spiral auger. It is carried by this auger to an endless band elevator which raises it and deposits it in the grain tank. The top of this elevator is shown

THAT CUTS AND THRESHES THE CORN

Grain tank

Elevator delivering chaff and tailings to be re-threshed

Spiked cylinder threshing out the grain

Feeder conveyor carrying grain to threshing cylinder

Tractor hauling harvester along

Shaft from tractor driving harvester machinery

Threshed grain falling to grain pan

Canvas elevator

Harvester moving forward in this direction →

Canvas conveyor

Cutters

Revolving arms pulling grain on to platform

in the drawing, and the bottom can also be seen against the spiral auger The chaff and tailings, when blown away fall through a sieve and are conveyed by another elevator, shown in the front of the drawing, to a chute through which they fall upon the feeder-conveyor, to pass under the spiked cylinder once again. This is to insure that any grain which may have been left with the chaff shall not be lost. As the straw comes from the spiked cylinder it is thrown upon racks, of which there are three sets. These carry it to the rear of the machine, and as it passes it is combed, and any chaff and tailings fall from the rack to the sieve ready to be conveyed up for re-threshing. Every particle of grain is shaken out into troughs underneath each rack section, and it flows down the troughs on to the grain pan, by which it is conveyed through the sieve to the chute ready for carrying up to the grain tank. The straw, after being thoroughly combed, is delivered at the rear of the machine. The grain tank can be emptied quickly into a motor truck or wagon. In some machines, instead of a grain tank, there is a platform where the grain can be fed into sacks as it is delivered by the elevator

THE INSIDE OF A GREAT MODERN STEAMSHIP

Wireless cabin

Steam steering gear controlled by Captain on bridge

Communication wire from Bridge

Wire from Bridge

Hot water returning through pipe to boilers

Steam pipes from boilers

Rudder shaft

Condenser

Low pressure turbine

Engineer's control platform

Reduction gearing

High pressure turbine

Astern turbine for reversing propellers

Rudder

Propeller turning clockwise to drive ship forward

A great modern steamship is one of the wonders of the world. Columbus would be astounded if he could revisit the world and see the kind of craft that now follow in his wake across the Atlantic. On these pages we see how a turbine steamship works. In this case the fuel used is coal, but many steamships now burn oil in their furnaces. The fire in the furnaces heats the water in the boilers and turns it into steam, which passes to the turbine engine. Here, mounted on a shaft, is a drum working in a cylinder. On the drum and on the inside of the cylinder are rows and rows of little vanes or blades firmly fixed in. The steam from the boiler strikes upon the first row of blades on the drum and is then deflected by the first row of blades on the cylinder, so that it next strikes against the drum's second row of blades. Then the second row of blades on the cylinder throws it against the third row on the drum, and so on. Thus

SHOWING HOW IT IS DRIVEN ACROSS THE SEA

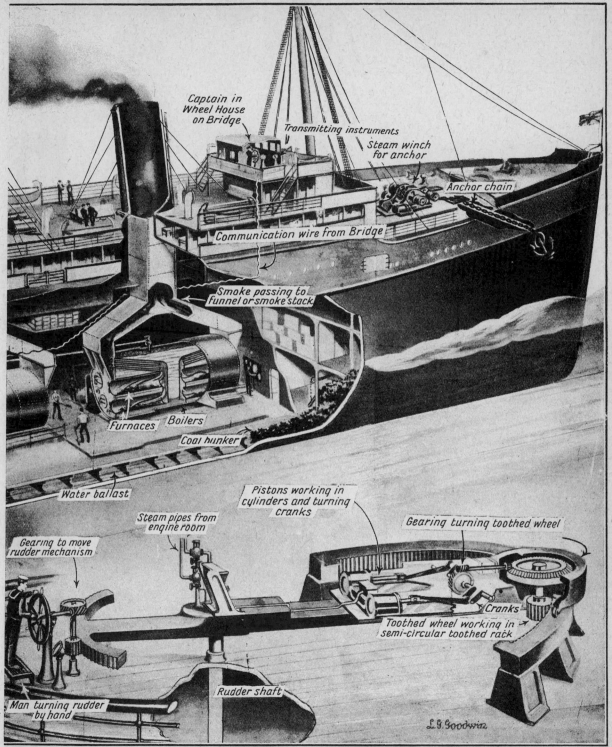

Captain in Wheel House on Bridge

Transmitting instruments

Steam winch for anchor

Anchor chain

Communication wire from Bridge

Smoke passing to funnel or smoke stack

Furnaces   Boilers

Coal bunker

Water ballast

Pistons working in cylinders and turning cranks

Gearing turning toothed wheel

Gearing to move rudder mechanism

Steam pipes from engine room

Cranks

Toothed wheel working in semi-circular toothed rack

Man turning rudder by hand

Rudder shaft

L. G. Goodwin

the steam rushes through the cylinder, striking on each row of blades on the drum and turning the drum round rapidly. As it revolves the drum a series of gear wheels turns the shaft with the propeller, and as this goes round it strikes the water and drives the ship forward. The drum is not of the same diameter throughout. It gets bigger towards the end, which means there are more blades in the rings the farther away they are from the steam entry. As the force of the steam gets spent towards the end of the cylinder it can act upon a larger number of blades and thus produce the same effect. In the turbines of a ship like the Mauretania there are more than a million and a half blades or vanes. The rudder is worked by steam gearing, operated by pistons in the stern of the ship, and this steering-gear is controlled by the captain from the bridge. It can also be worked by a man at the wheel in the stern.

HOW A SUBMARINE IS ABLE TO SINK

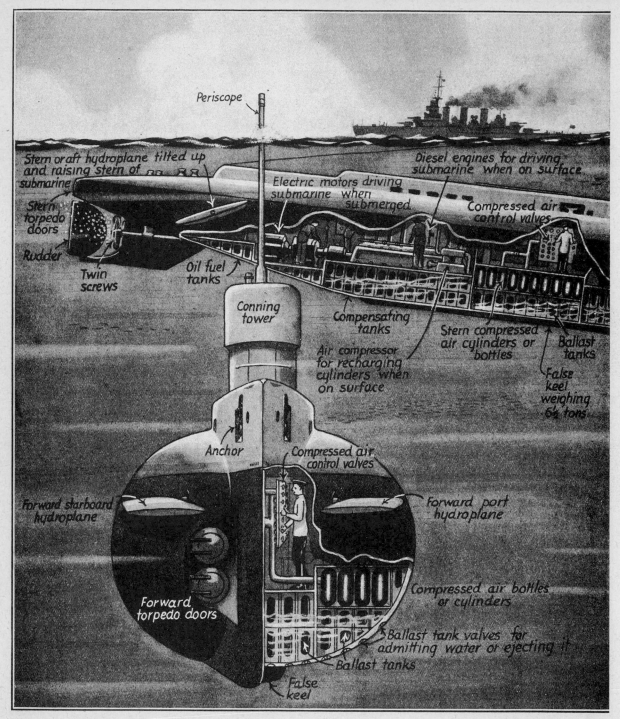

Periscope

Stern or aft hydroplane tilted up and raising stern of submarine

Diesel engines for driving submarine when on surface

Electric motors driving submarine when submerged

Compressed air control valves

Stern torpedo doors

Rudder

Twin screws

Oil fuel tanks

Conning tower

Compensating tanks

Air compressor for recharging cylinders when on surface

Stern compressed air cylinders or bottles

Ballast tanks

False keel weighing 6½ tons

Anchor

Compressed air control valves

Forward starboard hydroplane

Forward port hydroplane

Compressed air bottles or cylinders

Forward torpedo doors

Ballast tank valves for admitting water or ejecting it

Ballast tanks

False keel

This picture, going across two pages, explains how the submarine can sink and rise in the water. Normally, it is buoyant like an ordinary ship, but there are a number of ballast tanks into which water can be admitted, and as these fill up the submarine becomes less buoyant and sinks or dives. When the boat is about to dive, all hatches are closed and electrically-driven motors are switched on, the Diesel engines being stopped. The commanding officer takes up his position at a periscope and orders the main ballast tanks to be filled. The water is admitted through valves in the bottom, as in the lower left-hand drawing. At first, the air-escape valves in the tops of the tanks are closed so that the air displaced by the water cannot escape but becomes slightly compressed. At this stage the submarine does not go far down. To dive deeper the air valves are opened and water completely fills the ballast tanks. The submarine now submerges completely, and one periscope may be kept above the water. During this time the submarine has been travelling forward, driven by her motors. The hydroplanes or fins at either end help to force the submarine down and at the same time by manipulating the back fins the helmsman helps to prevent too much inclination. The commander, assisted by his first lieutenant, is in a position to instruct either the helmsman controlling the rudder or the helmsmen controlling the hydroplanes, two of which are forward and two aft. When the boat is on an even keel, these hydroplanes act as stabilisers, keeping the submarine steady in conjunction with a gyroscope. One or

AND RISE AT THE COMMANDER'S WILL

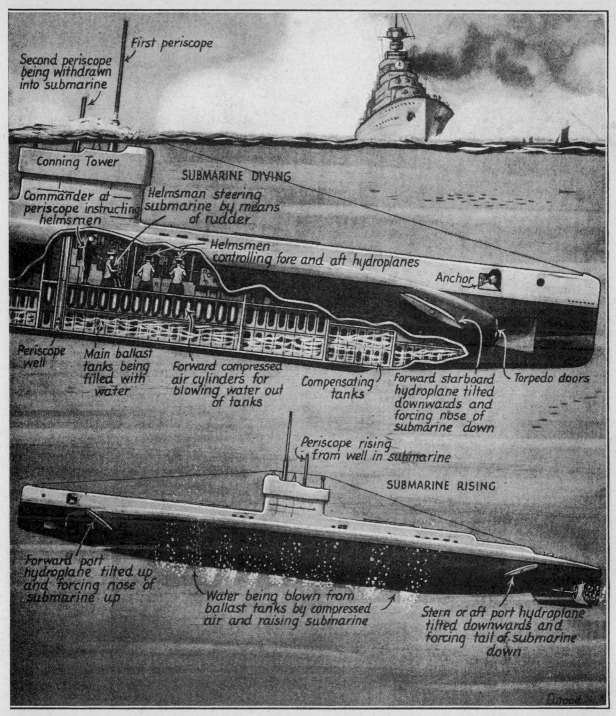

First periscope

Second periscope being withdrawn into submarine

Conning Tower

SUBMARINE DIVING

Commander at periscope instructing helmsmen

Helmsman steering submarine by means of rudder

Helmsmen controlling fore and aft hydroplanes

Anchor

Periscope well

Main ballast tanks being filled with water

Forward compressed air cylinders for blowing water out of tanks

Compensating tanks

Forward starboard hydroplane tilted downwards and forcing nose of submarine down

Torpedo doors

Periscope rising from well in submarine

SUBMARINE RISING

Forward port hydroplane tilted up and forcing nose of submarine up

Water being blown from ballast tanks by compressed air and raising submarine

Stern or aft port hydroplane tilted downwards and forcing tail of submarine down

both of the two periscopes can be slid down out of the way when the boat is submerged. There are two, in case one should get damaged. Some submarines have three. At either end of the main tanks are compensating tanks. For every gallon of fuel used while cruising, water is let in, but as water is heavier than oil the tanks have to be trimmed or compensated by the officers, who must exercise a constant vigilance to keep the boat level. This compensation is also necessary when a torpedo is released, and even when food is eaten by the men the tanks have to be compensated, because the food, though still in the submarine, has changed its place, being now in the men instead of in the stores. To rise, the water is blown from the ballast tanks by compressed air, and should the compressed air fail the tanks can be emptied by pumping. The compressed air is stored in cylinders at a pressure of 2,500 pounds per square inch. Should emergency arise a false keel, weighing several tons, can be dropped from the bottom of the submarine to lighten it when rising. When the air valves of the tanks are opened, compressed air rushes in and pushes the water out, the submarine rising and the hydroplanes being in a reverse position from that of diving. The cylinders contain enough compressed air for three submersions without being recharged. The cylinders are recharged when the boat is on the surface by an air compressor driven by the Diesel engines. The electric motors which drive the boat when submerged are supplied with current from batteries which can be recharged by the Diesel engines

Pipes from oil pumps

Rocker

Crude oil going to pumps

Cam lifting rocker

Compressed air pipe

Cooler

Eccentric

Air inlet

Piston

Inlet valve

Outlet valve

Valves

Water

Piston

Air receiver

Oil pump

Oil pump

Air compressor

Bearings

This picture, running across two pages, shows a Diesel engine and how it works. A Diesel engine is an internal combustion engine in which crude oil is used. Many ships are now fitted with Diesel engines. On the left can be seen an air compressor. It is worked by the driving shaft. Air is drawn in, and compressed when the piston goes up. This makes the air hot. It passes out through a coil, where it is cooled by cold water, and goes into an air receiver ready for use. The Diesel engine shown has six cylinders, and to start it the compressed air is let into the cylinders and drives the pistons. Once it has begun to move the engine works in the following way : In each cylinder in turn as the piston goes down ordinary air enters through an inlet above, a valve opening for this purpose. Then as the rotating shaft with its cranks drives the piston up once more, this air is compressed and gets hot. At the same time, just before the

USING CRUDE OIL FIRED BY HOT AIR

Compressed air pipe
Rockers

Oil needle lifted

Bevelled gear turning
cam shaft

Cam shaft

Exhaust outlet

Main exhaust pipe

Oil spray
entering
cylinder

Exhaust
valve open

Valves
closed

Air being compressed
by rising piston

Burnt gases
being driven
from cylinder

Oil firing, driving
piston down

Rod connecting main
driving shaft with
cam shaft Supports
are removed for
simplicity

Water

Water

Flywheel

Cranks

Driving shaft

Worm gear
turning
cam shaft

L.G.Goodwin

piston reaches the top of its journey, a fuel valve opens and a small quantity of heavy oil is sprayed into the cylinder by the compressed air from the receiver. At once the heat of the air in the cylinder, which is compressed by the rising piston, fires the oil, and the burnt gases expand until just before the end of the stroke, when an exhaust valve opens and these gases pass out. As soon as they have left the cylinder the exhaust valve shuts, and the air valve opens drawing in another charge of outside air, when the whole process is repeated. The same process is always happening in two of the cylinders, the cylinders working in pairs. Four of the cylinders are here shown uncovered, the other two being at the left of the engine. The fly-wheel on the right keeps the shaft rotating steadily. The valves are worked by cams on a cam shaft. The fuel oil is supplied from a large tank above the engine and the engine is kept cool by cold water

HOW STEEL IS MADE BY THE OPEN HEARTH

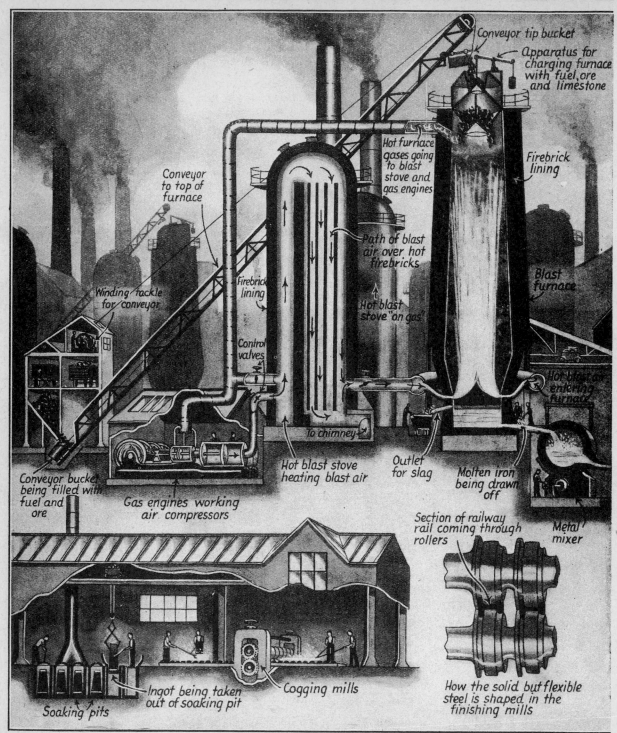

Conveyor tip bucket

Apparatus for charging furnace with fuel, ore and limestone

Hot furnace gases going to blast stove and gas engines

Firebrick lining

Conveyor to top of furnace

Path of blast air over hot firebricks

Hot blast stove "on gas"

Blast furnace

Firebrick lining

Winding tackle for conveyor

Control valves

Hot blast air entering furnace

Conveyor bucket being filled with fuel and ore

To chimney

Hot blast stove heating blast air

Outlet for slag

Molten iron being drawn off

Gas engines working air compressors

Metal mixer

Section of railway rail coming through rollers

Ingot being taken out of soaking pit

Cogging mills

How the solid but flexible steel is shaped in the finishing mills

Soaking pits

In this picture running across two pages we see the whole method of making steel by the Open Hearth Process, which has largely superseded the Bessemer Process. As seen on the left, fuel and iron ore are conveyed to the top of a blast furnace, where they are tipped in through a cone-shaped flap. A second flap is kept closed while this is going on, and then the top flap is closed and the bottom one opened, allowing the ore and fuel to fall into the furnace. The double flap prevents the hot gases from escaping. The ore is subjected to great heat in the furnace by a blast of hot air and gas from a blast stove. Molten iron runs to the bottom of the furnace, and is drawn off as required. To create the blast the hot gases from the furnace are conveyed to the blast stove, and also to gas engines, thereby driving the air compressors which supply the blast. The interior fire-bricks of the blast stove are made white-hot by the passage of gas through them, known technically as "on gas." When the valves are reversed air is pumped through called "on air," and compressed air is made hot ready to enter the blast furnace. There are two stoves to each blast furnace, one working "on air," and the other "on gas." These are reversed each half hour. The slag in the furnace being lighter than molten iron floats on top and is drawn off. To make steel the molten iron is conveyed to a metal mixer, where it settles, while certain gases are given off. Then it is turned into the open hearth furnace, and subjected to great heat given by blasts of combustible

PROCESS, THE MOST USUAL SYSTEM TO-DAY

Travelling ladle lined with firebrick

Rails

Ingot mould being filled with molten steel from ladle

Charging machine which charges furnace with steel scrap and ore

Hot air and gases entering furnace

Firebrick

Firedoor

Sand

Exhaust air and gases heating regenerators

Gas passing over hot firebricks

Air passing over hot firebricks

Slag tip

Ingot on way to soaking pits.

Gas producer

To chimney

Gas regenerator

Air regenerator

Row of ingots

Travelling ladle

Control valves for reversing flow of air and gas

Air entering air pipe from air compressors

L.Wood

gas and compressed air. It is mixed with scrap steel, carbon and other substances according to the kind of steel required. An electric charging machine is thrust into the furnace and the materials are tipped out. In the Open Hearth method the operators have complete control over the metal throughout the process. Hot compressed air and gases are supplied to the open hearth furnace in the same way as to the blast furnace, four regenerators working on the same principle as the blast stove. Gas is produced this time by a gas producer and, after passing over white-hot fire-bricks in the regenerator, goes to the furnace. In the meantime compressed air has been passing through another regenerator and the two are blown into the furnace together. After going through the furnace the hot air and gases pass to another set of regenerators, where on their way to the chimney they give up their heat to the fire-bricks. When these are sufficiently hot the control valves are reversed, and gas and air now enter the furnace through these regenerators, the whole process being reversed. The resulting steel is drawn off into a travelling ladle, which fills a number of ingot moulds with molten steel. The process is shown in the top right-hand drawing. The moulds are then taken to what are known as soaking pits, holes lined with fire-brick, where they are kept at a constant temperature, to insure uniform temperature in each mould. The steel ingots are then put through the cogging and roughing mills, where they are rolled out, and finally go to finishing mills, where the steel is rolled into rails or girders as required

A BIG COAL MINE WITH THE LID OFF:

Winding gear

Coal being tippled on to screen

Tipplers

Cage guides or rails

Double decked cage

Small coal dropping on to moving belt for hand-picking

Pit shaft

Stables

Air pipe from surface

Disc coal-cutter at work

Cage

Until the early part of the present century coal was king. Nearly all the motive power of the world was obtained from this form of fuel, in which has been stored up for millions of years a vast amount of the Sun's energy. The coal is dug out of the earth, and as it is burned its energy is released, so that with its heat we can make steam to drive ships and trains and machinery. We also use the coal to warm our homes. In this picture we see what a coal mine is like. Every coal mine has two shafts, one, called the down-cast shaft, for the miners to pass up and down and for the coal to be hauled out, and the other, the up-cast shaft, for ventilation, a powerful fan driving a current of air constantly through the workings. The men work along the seams of coal at different levels, digging out the coal and sending it to the shaft so that it can be hauled to the surface. For this hauling there is a winding gear worked by a

DIGGING OUT THE FUEL FOR OUR FIRES

Boiler

Winding engine

Fan drawing stale air from mine

Electricity generator

Air compressor to work cutting machines in mine

Ventilating shaft

Coal seam

Pit props

Coal seam

Pillars of coal left to prevent mine falling in

Electric light

Box of cartridges

Props for new workings

Drilling hole for blasting

Main road of mine

Fossil trees of Carboniferous Age

Safety lamps

L.G. Goodwin

powerful engine, and the power to drive the engine is obtained from the coal of the pit. As the coal is dug out, the roof has to be propped up with wooden props. In some mines holes are drilled and blasting cartridges fired to break up the coal, but this cannot be done in all pits. In many modern pits mechanical cutters worked by compressed air are now used. Up to the present, however, most of the coal mined has been dug out by miners with small pickaxes. In the old days children and women used to push the trucks along the workings to the bottom of the shaft, but now horses or electric power do this. Some mines are lighted by electric lamps, but in most the safety lamp is still used. When they reach the top the trucks of coal are run into tipplers, which turn them up and shoot the coal on to screens for sorting into sizes. The coal then goes into railway wagons and is ready for sale.

Volume III

WONDERS OF LIFE

Contents—Volume III. Wonders of Life

Book 11

LIVING CREATURES *in* PREHISTORIC AGES

These pictures are the first of a series of reconstructions by Miss Betty Nation, showing what life was like on the Earth in past ages, Here we see life in the Cambrian and Ordovician periods, twenty to thirty million years ago. Life probably began with one-celled plants and animals in the shallow waters. As time went on there developed sponges and jellyfish, and corals and crusted animals called trilobites. and gastropods with single shells and bivalved molluscs. There were also barnacles and shrimp-like crustaceans and crinoids or sea-lilies. Vegetation included seaweeds, and on land primitive horse-tails and club-mosses. There were also possibly a few land insects

This picture shows life in the Silurian period, which began about 18,000,000 years ago, and lasted for some 3,000,000 years. Life was still mostly in the water, although on land the club-mosses and plants like ferns were developed. Sponges, not unlike those which we have to-day; began to appear, and reef-building corals. The sea lilies became larger and finer, and starfishes became more complex. Sea-urchins appeared, and various shell forms multiplied. Creatures with spiral shells of turret form first appeared in this age, and trilobites became more widely distributed. Early forms of king-crab and sea-scorpion were found, and there were fishes of the shark form

LIFE ON THE EARTH 15 MILLION YEARS AGO

In the left-hand picture we see what life was like in the Devonian period of the Earth's history, about 15 million years ago. Shark-like fishes had increased in variety and size from the Silurian period pictured on page 150. There were other fishes, known as ganoids, with enamelled scales and tails quite different from modern fishes' tails. There were also creatures with partially armoured bodies and toothed jaws. Sea-urchins, molluscs, star-fishes, sea-lilies, corals and sponges all abounded. Plant life was abundant in the sea, and ferns and plants allied to the club-mosses and horse-tails grew on land. On the right we see the life of the Carboniferous period about 13 million years ago. This was when the forests that formed the coal were flourishing. The vegetation consisted of huge ferns, horse-tails and club mosses as big as trees. Insects, myriapods, scorpions, and spiders crawled about, and the sea contained fishes related to our modern skates. But the most notable development was the appearance of amphibian creatures that could live in water and also on land. They resembled lizards and salamanders and one of them, known as the labyrinthodon, was as strong and big as our modern crocodiles

LIFE ON THE EARTH EIGHT MILLION YEARS AGO

On the left our artist, Miss Betty Nation, shows the kind of life that existed in the Permian period of the world's history, perhaps 8 million years ago, when there was a great uplifting of the Earth's crust, and Africa and South America first appeared. It was the age when giant tree-ferns flourished, but cone-bearing trees began to appear. Amphibians were developing into reptiles. These Permian reptiles were only a few feet long, but they were the beginning of life on land. Some of them had spiny crests down their backs. Fish, which in earlier ages had been the highest living creatures, had now lost the lead. In many Permian fishes the tail was becoming symmetrical, as in our living fishes of to-day. The Permian age brought to a close the Palaeozoic or earliest life epoch of the Earth's history. On the right we see life in the Triassic period, which succeeded, and which began perhaps 7 million years ago. Of course, geologists vary enormously in estimating the duration of the various geological periods, but we have taken a conservative estimate. In the Triassic age there were many kinds of trees as well as ferns and in addition to invertebrate types many new vertebrates were appearing. There were ichthyosaurs or fish-lizards, large land reptiles, and the very earliest mammals. Of the form of these mammals, however, we know nothing

LIFE ON THE EARTH SIX MILLION YEARS AGO

In this picture we are given some idea of what life was like on the Earth in the Jurassic period, which some geologists tell us began about six million years ago. Reptiles dominated the world, and there were giant dinosaurs, including the famous diplodocus, a creature as long as a small street. Some of these giant reptiles were vegetarian and others carnivorous. Living forms were never so grotesque as during this age. Several dinosaurs are shown, and on the left behind the tree is a stegosaurus. Some of the crocodiles lived in the sea. There were great flying lizards or "dragons of the air," and by the end of the Jurassic Age the earliest bird was seen, known as archaeopteryx. It was about the size of a crow, and had claws on its wings. Vegetation consisted of coniferous trees, ferns and cycads

LIFE ON THE EARTH FOUR MILLION YEARS AGO

In the Cretaceous Period, about four million years ago, there were still great dinosaurs living on the Earth, but the supremacy of the reptile was on the decline. One of the most notable was the triceratops, seen here with two large horns on the forehead and a smaller one on the snout, hence its name, meaning three-horned. There were also iguanodons, one being shown with its head and forepart raised, and another dinosaur was the polacanthus, whose back was protected by a double row of plates. Great flying dragons flew in the air, and toothed birds, which spent much of their time in the water, were common. Mammals had made little progress

LIFE ON THE EARTH 3,000,000 YEARS AGO

By the time the Eocene Age dawned great changes had come to the life of the world. Many of the old forms of reptiles had passed away for ever, and the mammals had become the dominant type. The remote ancestor of the horse, known as hyracotherium, a little animal the size of a fox terrier (bottom right of picture) made its appearance, and also a curious animal (bottom left) known as phenacodus, which had a tail like a tiger's and combined some of the characteristics of the deer, pig, tapir, horse and ape. In the picture, above the phenacodus, we see the horned amblypod, an animal of the rhinoceros type. Above this on the left we see the arsinoitherium also something like a rhinoceros. There were two forerunners of the elephant, one the moeritherium (top left of picture) about three feet high, and the palæomastodon, an animal twice that size, with small tusks and a short trunk. Pigs bigger than wild boars were beginning to appear. One seen on the right of the picture is called the elotherium. Crocodiles, alligators, lizards and snakes were living, and a large variety of sea life, including sharks much like those that live to-day. In vegetation there were trees like our present-day trees, such as oaks, chestnuts, yews, walnuts, limes, alders, willows, firs, pines and cypresses

LIFE ON THE EARTH 1,750,000 YEARS AGO

Life in the Oligocene Age shown in this picture was becoming in form much more like that which we see on the Earth to-day. There were many new forms of birds resembling present-day forms, such as the ancestors of our modern grebes and divers. There were geese of modern type, as seen at the top of the picture. Among rhinoceros-like animals were the brontotherium, with two horns on the nose, as shown on the right, and the acerotherium (in the middle of the picture), more like the rhinoceros of to-day. Camel-like animals, seen at the bottom right, were developing, and also weasel forms, shown lower down. The pig-like animal at the bottom of the picture, called the hyopotamus, seems to have chewed the cud. On the left of this is the mesohippus, a small ancestor of the horse. Above this we see a group of hyracodon. This animal was about the size of a pony, but in form it was much nearer the rhinoceros, although more lightly built. In the water there were early whales, and among the vegetation of Europe were palm trees, olives and the ebony

LIFE ON THE EARTH 1,250,000 YEARS AGO

In this picture Miss Betty Nation has reconstructed the life found on the Earth in the Miocene Period, about a million-and-a-quarter years ago, according to some geologists. The temperature of Europe was getting cooler, and plants more like those of Europe to-day flourished. There were, for instance, irises and poppies and pinks and violets. It was the age of the sabre-toothed tiger. Giraffes had not yet appeared in this age, but there was a camel-like animal with a giraffe-like neck, which enabled it to feed on the foliage of tall trees. Animals of the elephant family were growing more like the elephants of to-day, and one, the tetrabelodon, had a very long under-jaw with tusks of the modern type. A hare-like animal, but much larger than our hares, is shown at the bottom, left. It is called the toxodont, and a burrowing creature shown on the right, known as a mylagaulus, had a horn on its snout. Ape-like creatures were appearing. One of these, seen on the left, called pliopithicus, was something like the gibbon of to-day. There were some birds very much like our marabou storks, auks, gulls, guillemots and curlews

LIFE ON THE EARTH 250,000 YEARS AGO

In this picture, which is the last of the series showing life on the Earth in past ages, we see the kind of animals that lived a quarter of a million years ago in the late Pliocene and the Pleistocene Ages. In the top right-hand corner we see the great Irish deer and, below, the mammoth with its woolly coat and great tusks. On the left is the woolly rhinoceros with the glyptodont, an armadillo-like animal, beneath and the camel-like macrauchenia in the middle of the picture. In the bottom left-hand corner is the hippidium, a desert horse whose remains have been found in South America. At the beginning of the Pleistocene Age the cold in the northern hemisphere was increasing, and a large part of Europe was covered with snow and huge glaciers. The elephant and rhinoceros had developed woolly coats to resist the cold, and many other animals had migrated farther south. The mammoth had crossed to North America by the land bridge where the Behring Strait now flows and, as we see, Man, the most recent of all animals, had at last appeared on the Earth

Book 12

▼▼▼▼▼▼▼▼▼▼

MARVELS *of*
PLANT LIFE

▲▲▲▲▲▲▲▲ ▲▲▲▲▲▲

A PETRIFIED FOREST OF THE FAR DISTANT PAST

One of the most interesting relics of a distant geological age is the petrified forest of Arizona, where, lying about on the surface of the ground, are to be seen the fossilised trunks of giant trees. For thousands of years these were buried and were gradually changed into stone thereby being preserved for our inspection. Here is one trunk forming a natural bridge

After these trees had been buried for generations and had become fossilised, the land was upheaved, and the wind and water, assisted by the action of rivers, wore away the soil till the petrified trees were left open to the sky. They now tell the story of their past

THE BIGGEST LIVING THING IN THE WORLD

What is the biggest living thing in the world? Most people would answer " a whale," or perhaps " an elephant," but neither reply would be correct. The biggest living thing in the world is this giant sequoia tree, which forms one of the Mammoth Grove in the Sequoia National Park, California. It is over 300 feet high, and contains enough timber to make 30,000 million matches, or a box of 16 for every inhabitant of the world. This wonderful grove of trees in California contains not only the biggest living thing in the world, but the oldest. Some of the giant trees are believed to have been growing for more than 4,000 years. It is a marvellous thought that there should be still living in the world trees that were flourishing when Moses was playing as a little child by the banks of the Nile.

STRANGE FREAKS OF PLANT GROWTH

There are plant as well as animal freaks and here are some.   1 and 2 are specimens of fasciated growth in asparagus—that is, where separate parts grow together in fasces or bundles; 3 shows potato tubers growing on a leaf stem ; 4, a foxglove with several flowers growing together; 5, a pitcher-shaped pelargonium leaf; 6, twin oak trees ; 7, yew leaves growing together spirally; 8, a turnip with leaves growing inside it ; 9, a dandelion with many florets ; 10, a rose with a stem extended from the blossom ; 11, twin mushrooms; 12, a pear with strangely swelled axis ; 13, a strawberry with a leaf stem growing from it ; 14, a rose with the sepals as leaves ; 15 and 16, apple twins ; 17, six broccoli heads on one stalk ; 18, polyanthus leaves and flowers mixed up ; 19, twin teasel flowers ; 20, an apple with a swollen stalk ; 21, a cabbage with leaves reduced to mid-ribs ; 22, a rose with sepals replaced by leaves ; 23 and 27, unusual developments of fern fronds ; 24, a strange pink ; 25, a primrose flower changed into leaves ; 26, a fasciated growth of lettuce ; 27, see 23

PLANTS THAT CATCH AND EAT INSECTS

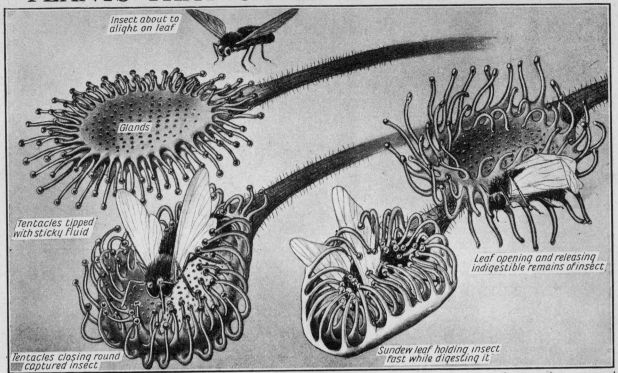

Insect about to alight on leaf

Glands

Tentacles tipped with sticky fluid

Leaf opening and releasing indigestible remains of insect

Tentacles closing round captured insect

Sundew leaf holding insect fast while digesting it

There is a British plant, the sundew, shown here magnified, which feeds on insects. It has flat, round leaves whose margins are covered with short bristles, each ending in a knob that exudes a sticky liquid. When an insect touches one of these knobs it is held fast, and the hairs at once close over it. Then from a number of glands the plant pours out a juice by which parts of the insect are digested, the liquid containing the digested portions being absorbed and nourishing the plant. Afterwards the leaf opens and the remains drop out.

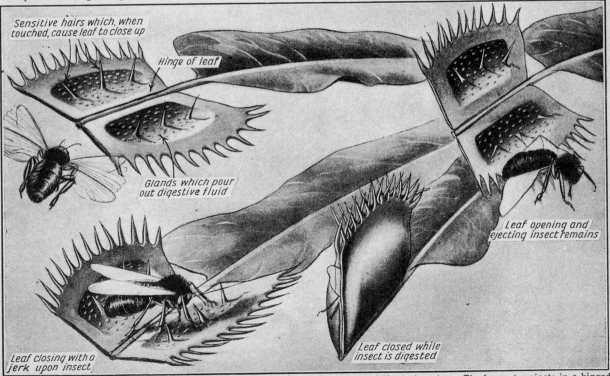

Sensitive hairs which, when touched, cause leaf to close up

Hinge of leaf

Glands which pour out digestive fluid

Leaf opening and ejecting insect remains

Leaf closing with a jerk upon insect

Leaf closed while insect is digested

Another plant which catches and devours insects is the Venus Fly-trap, a native of North America. The leaves terminate in a hinged portion surrounded by a fringe of bristles. On the inside of each half of the trap grow three short sensitive hairs, and directly these are touched by an insect, the two hinged sections close up with a snap, like a rat-trap, and the imprisoned insect is then digested by juices.

THE MANY DIFFERENT OUTLINES OF THE LEAVES

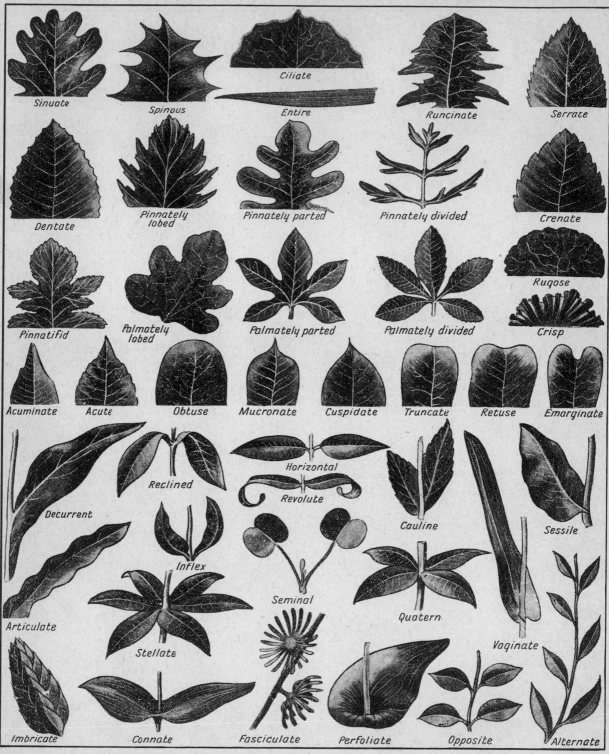

Botanists have classified the leaves according to their margins and their tips, and in this page we see the different forms and their names. Sinuate means "wavy-edged"; Ciliate, "fringed with hairs"; Runcinate and Serrate, "saw-like"; Dentate, "toothed"; Pinnate and Pinnatifid, "like a feather"; Crenate, "notched"; Palmate, "like a hand"; Rugose, "wrinkled"; Acuminate, "sharpened"; Mucronate, "sharp-pointed"; Cuspidate, "pointed"; Retuse, "blunted"; and Emarginate, "notched." The lower pictures show different ways in which the leaf is attached to the stem. Decurrent means "running-down"; Cauline, "belonging to the stem"; Sessile, "sitting"; Inflex, "incurved"; Seminal, "seed-like"; Vaginate, "sheathed"; Imbricate, "overlapped"

THE MANY DIFFERENT SHAPES OF LEAVES

Elliptical or Oval — Oblong — Orbicular — Cuneate — Spathulate — Cloven — Canaliculate — Triquetrous — Acinaciform — Acerose — Ovate — Obovate — Subulate — Reniform — Obcordate — Lunulate — Cordate — Linear — Lanceolate — Triangular or Deltoid — Hastate — Sagittate — Plicate — Trilobate or Trifid — Praemorse — Lobate — Peltate — Dolabriform — Erose — Quinquangular — Auriculate — Partite — Pinnate — Panduriform — Lyrate — Bipinnate — Palmatisect — Bilobate or Bifid — Tridentate — Paripinnate — Tripinnate — Conjugate — Ternate — Pinnatifid — Imparipinnate — Biternate — Decussate — Digitate — Palmate — Pedate — Bijugate — Verticillate

Leaves are a very important part of a plant, for it is by means of them that it breathes and takes in carbon dioxide and oxygen from the air.   Leaves vary much in form and texture.   We know that a grass leaf is a long blade and a nasturtium leaf almost round.   Some leaves present an unbroken surface, while others are indented.   The different kinds of leaves are grouped according to shape, and botanists have given them special names.   On this page we see 52 leaves, with the correct names given to their particular forms.   Some names are from Latin words, like Digitate, from digitus, meaning a finger.   Others have formidable names like Quinquangular, which means having five angles.   The separate parts of divided leaves, though looking like individual leaves, are only leaflets or parts of the one leaf

HOW THE PLANTS PROTECT THEMSELVES

Holly · Thistle · Barberry · Linnaea · Bramble · Cuphea · Hedgehog cactus · Plumbago · Dog Rose · Lonicera · Stinging Nettle · Organ Cactus · Fennel · Hound's-Tongue · Bearberry · Bottle-grass

Plants have all sorts of ways of protecting themselves from animals that would prey upon them. The stinging hairs of the nettle form a good defence, as do hairs on many other plants like the lonicera or honeysuckle, which either keep undesirable insects away or warn grazing animals by giving them an unpleasant sensation in the mouth. Some plants have spiny leaves, like the holly and thistles, or thorns, like the furze and rose and bramble. The cactuses have in some cases thickened their skins as a protection, and in others covered themselves with spines. There are plants like certain grasses which have developed sharp, serrated edges that cut those who handle them, while others like the Linnaea borealis and plumbago have sticky glands or, like the cuphea, sticky bristles. Other plants like fennel and hound's-tongue warn off enemies by their strong odour. Many of these protective devices of plants are illustrated in these pictures of plants

VARIOUS WAYS IN WHICH PLANTS CLIMB

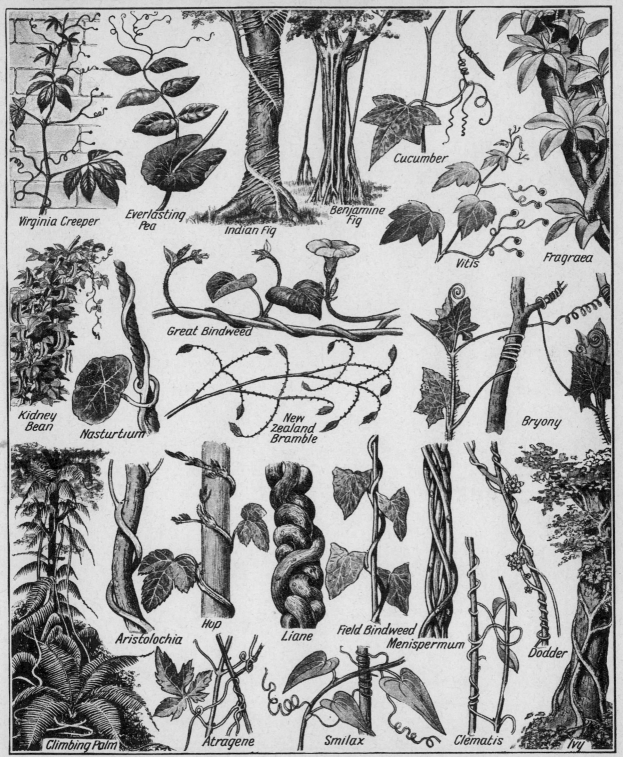

Virginia Creeper

Everlasting Pea

Indian Fig

Benjamine Fig

Cucumber

Vitis

Fragraea

Kidney Bean

Nasturtium

Great Bindweed

New Zealand Bramble

Bryony

Climbing Palm

Aristolochia

Hop

Liane

Field Bindweed

Menispermum

Dodder

Atragene

Smilax

Clematis

Ivy

There are many plants which have special devices for climbing up towards the sunlight, and some of these are shown in these pictures. In certain cases the plant's growing stem rises, and as it does so turns round in a circle seeking for a support to grasp. Having found one it continues to twine spirally up the support. Other plants throw out tendrils which grasp at any support, and hold on while the growing stem continues to rise. Then there are plants that develop little suckers which have the power of holding to tree trunks or walls, and other plants produce little rootlets that find their way into cracks and crevices and support the plant as it grows. Climbing plants are often the enemies of the trees to which they cling or round which they twine, for they strangle or sap the nourishment from their host

THE MANY DIFFERENT FORMS OF FRUITS

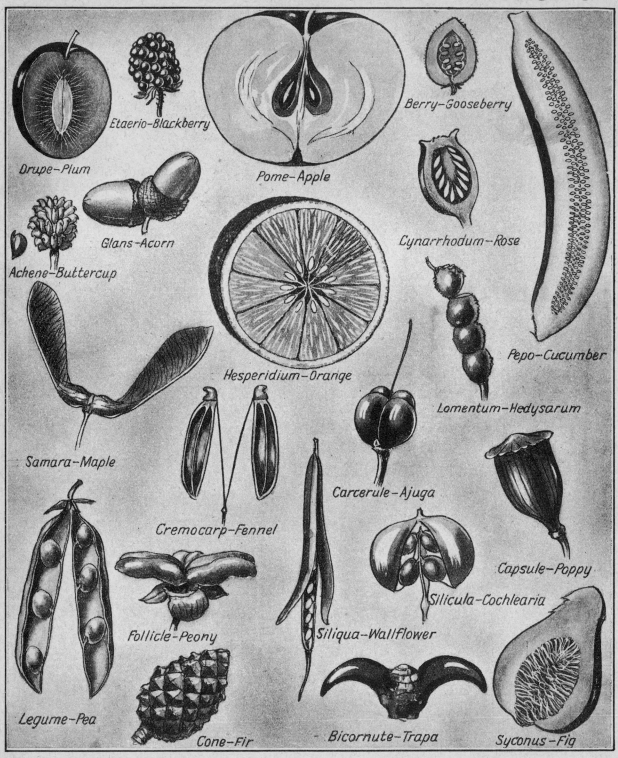

Drupe—Plum · Etaerio—Blackberry · Pome—Apple · Berry—Gooseberry · Glans—Acorn · Achene—Buttercup · Cynarrhodum—Rose · Hesperidium—Orange · Pepo—Cucumber · Samara—Maple · Lomentum—Hedysarum · Cremocarp—Fennel · Carcerule—Ajuga · Capsule—Poppy · Follicle—Peony · Siliqua—Wallflower · Silicula—Cochlearia · Legume—Pea · Cone—Fir · Bicornute—Trapa · Syconus—Fig

In these pictures we see the many different forms which the fruits of plants take, and the names which botanists have given to them. Stone fruits are known as drupes, the word being from the Latin name for an olive. An etaerio is a fruit composed of a number of drupes grouped together. An achene is a small fruit with the seed free in the interior, and a glans is the name for such fruits as nuts and acorns. A cynarrhodum is an etaerio of achenes contained within a hollow receptacle. A samara is a winged fruit, and a capsule is a fruit that opens so that the seeds may fall out. A legume is a pod. A siliqua is a long capsule that splits longitudinally, while a silicula is a short and broad siliqua. A bicornute fruit is one with two horns, and a syconus is a receptacle with the fruits closed in

WHAT FAMILIAR FRUITS ARE LIKE INSIDE

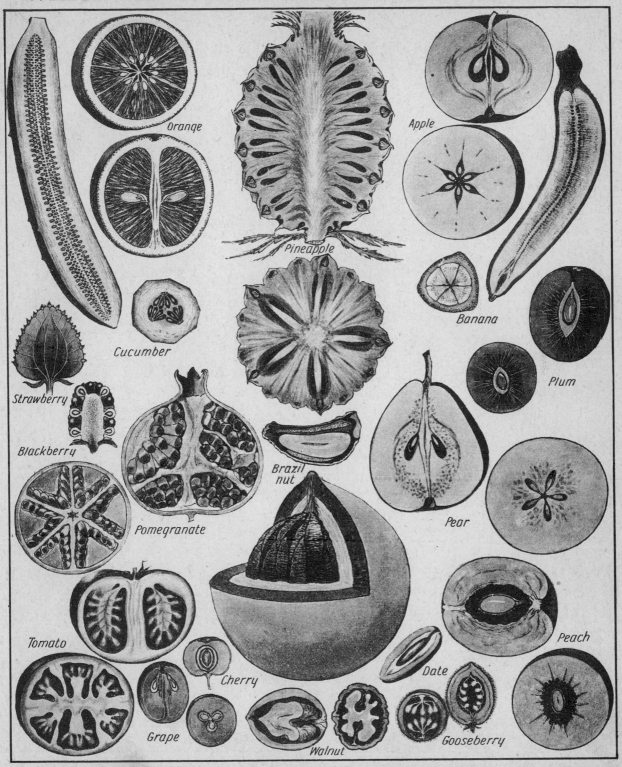

Orange
Pineapple
Apple
Banana
Plum
Cucumber
Strawberry
Blackberry
Brazil nut
Pomegranate
Pear
Peach
Tomato
Cherry
Date
Grape
Walnut
Gooseberry

On this page are given pictures showing what eighteen of our familiar fruits are like inside. In most cases double sections are given, that is, each fruit is shown cut down longitudinally or the long way, and also cut across. In the case of the strawberry, blackberry, Brazil nut, cherry and date, longitudinal sections only are given. Brazil nuts are really sections of a fruit which is large in size and has a very hard case outside ; in fact, a Brazil nut falling from a tree on to a man's head might stun him. The Brazil nuts in their shells which we buy in the shops are packed inside this hard case something like the sections of an orange. The pips and kernels of fruits are seeds

HOW THE LEAVES OF TREES UNFOLD THEMSELVES

The unfolding of the leaves of trees is a very interesting study, and in spring it is well worth while watching this going on in the various trees from day to day. We shall notice that when the leaf-bud opens the leaves are very carefully packed together, and the method of packing varies in different trees. In the beech tree, for example, the green portions of the young leaves before they open are deeply folded, and the veins are close to one another, so that the silken hairs which appear only on the margins and on the veins overlap and appear to cover the whole leaf. The reason for this is that the green tissue, having a delicate silken covering, is protected from the Sun until the outer skin or epidermis is thick enough to afford protection, and then the folds of the leaf flatten out, and the leaf takes up a horizontal instead of a vertical position, turning the lower surface away from the Sun so that the hairs are of no further use. In its young days a leaf is tender, and needs some protective device to prevent it from being withered by the Sun. In some cases Nature provides a varnish for this purpose. Many leaves when they first emerge are crumpled or rolled. On this page we see how various leaves unfold

HOW PLANTS GO TO SLEEP AT NIGHT-TIME

Many plants may be said to go to sleep at night and, like ourselves, their leaves and flowers take up a different position from what they do in the daytime. We lie down instead of sitting or standing, and often we curl ourselves up in bed to keep warm. The leaves of many plants also close up at night, to protect themselves from frost. In such plants as the clover the leaves droop, and it has been found that when some leaves on a plant are prevented from folding or drooping at night and the plant is exposed to frost, only the folded leaves escape, the others being killed. But as many tropical plants also fold their leaves at night the plant probably has some other purpose in taking this sleeping attitude besides protection from cold. Flowers in the same way close up their petals, or droop, to keep out the cold. On this page the flowers and leaves of a number of plants are shown by day and by night

THE DIFFERENT KINDS OF PLANT ROOTS

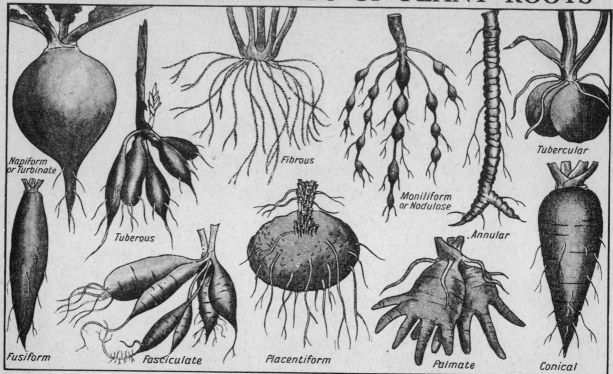

The roots form a very important part of a plant, for they perform two essential duties. First of all it is by the roots that the plant adjusts itself to the soil and obtains the necessary support to grow in a suitable position, and further it is through the roots that the plant absorbs water and food solutions for its nourishment. Sometimes the roots also act as storehouses of food for the plant, and in that case they take on a specially enlarged form which will enable them to hold large reserves of food. Botanists have divided plant roots into classes according to their form, and in these pictures we see a typical example of each form. Napiform means turnip-shaped, and turbinate shaped like a top. Tuberous means swollen; fibrous means having fibres; moniliform means shaped like a necklace and nodulose is knotted. Annular is from the Latin word for a ring, and an annular root is made up of rings. Tubercular is from the Latin word for a little knob. Fusiform means spindle-shaped. Fasciculate is from the Latin word for a little bundle. Placentiform means shaped like a cheese-cake ; palmate is like the palm of one's hand, and conical is, of course, like a cone

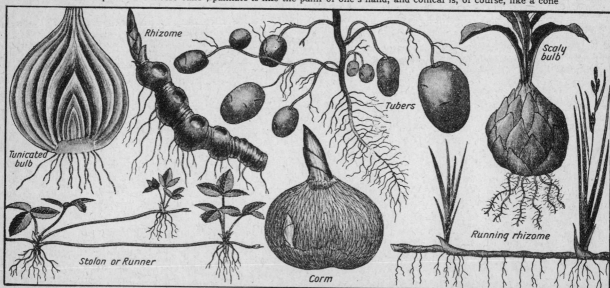

In many plants the stem takes on a curious form which is often suggestive of a root, but is not really a root at all. In these pictures are shown some of these root-like stems. A bulb is really a modified leaf bud with fleshy scales partly or wholly buried in the soil. Tunicated means covered with a tunic or membrane, and a tunicated bulb is one composed of numerous concentric coats like an onion. A scaly bulb, of course, consists of a number of scales. A corm, which is from the Greek word for a stem, is the swollen bulb-like base of a stem. Tuber means a swelling, and, of course, our common potatoes are tubers. A rhizome, which comes from the Greek word for root, is a prostrate or subterranean stem giving out leaves at growing points and rootlets from its own surface. A stolon, which is from the Latin word for a shoot, is a trailing branch striking into the earth and rooting, a fresh plant growing from each new root

THE DIFFERENT KINDS OF PLANT STEMS

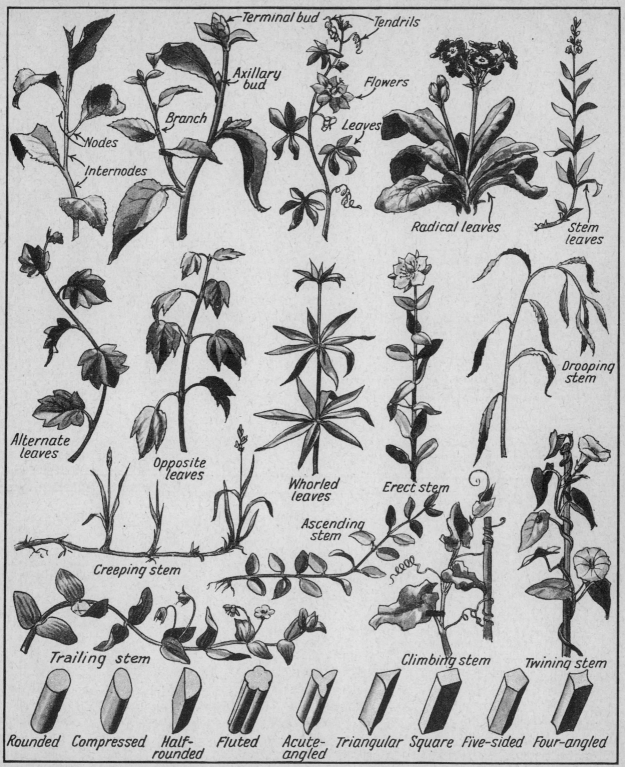

Terminal bud
Tendrils
Axillary bud
Flowers
Branch
Leaves
Nodes
Internodes
Radical leaves
Stem leaves

Alternate leaves
Opposite leaves
Whorled leaves
Erect stem
Drooping stem
Ascending stem
Creeping stem
Trailing stem
Climbing stem
Twining stem

Rounded Compressed Half-rounded Fluted Acute-angled Triangular Square Five-sided Four-angled

The stems of plants, are found in a great variety of forms, as shown here. First we see the parts of the stem. The point from which a leaf grows is called a node, and the portion between two nodes is called an internode. From the main stem many plants give off branches, and the buds have special names according to the places where they appear. Some stems have not only leaves and flowers but tendrils, which enable them to climb. When leaves grow along a stem they are called stem leaves, and when they start near the ground they are known as radical leaves. Stems have many shapes, and sections of these, with their names, are given

VEGETATION AT DIFFERENT HEIGHTS AND LATITUDES

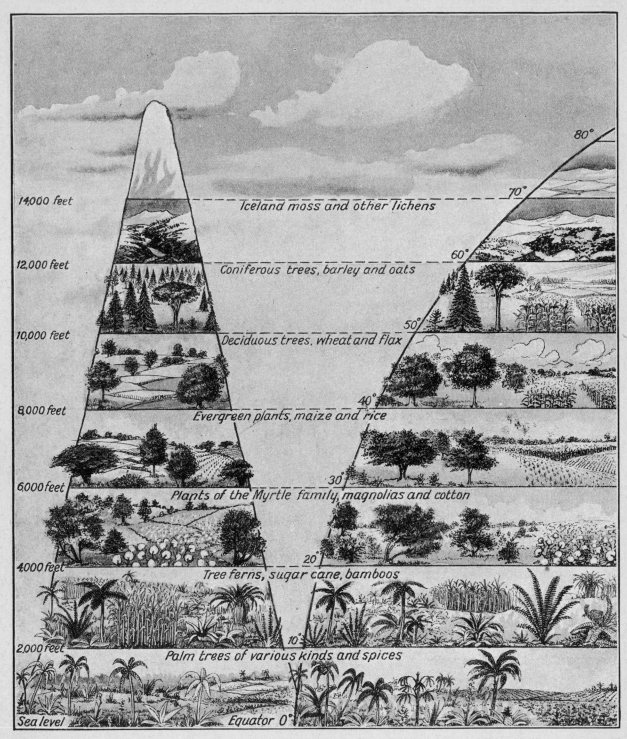

This picture-diagram shows us how the vegetation of the world varies according to latitude and altitude. Speaking generally, between 10° north and 10° south of the Equator grow such plants as palms and spices, and these also grow on mountains on the Equator up to a height of 2,000 feet. Between 10° and 20° latitude are found tree ferns, sugar-cane and bamboos, and this applies also to the mountains between 2,000 and 4,000 feet up. From 20° to 30° the vegetation changes again, and we find members of the myrtle family, with cotton, growing. These also grow between 4,000 and 6,000 feet up. Between 30° and 40° we find evergreens, maize and rice, and these thrive on the mountains from 6,000 to 8,000 feet up. Next come the trees that lose their leaves in winter, with wheat and flax. These thrive between 40° and 50° latitude, and also on the mountain from 8,000 to 10,000 feet up. From 50° to 60°, and from 10,000 to 12,000 feet up are coniferous trees, with barley and oats. From 60° to 70° and from 12,000 to 14,000 feet up are the lichens, and beyond that height and latitude plants are not found at all. Of course local climate conditions vary these figures in certain areas but the picture gives a general idea of the similarities of latitude and altitude in plant distribution

Book 13

The STRANGEST FISH in the SEA

HOW THE FISH OF THE SEA ARE CAUGHT

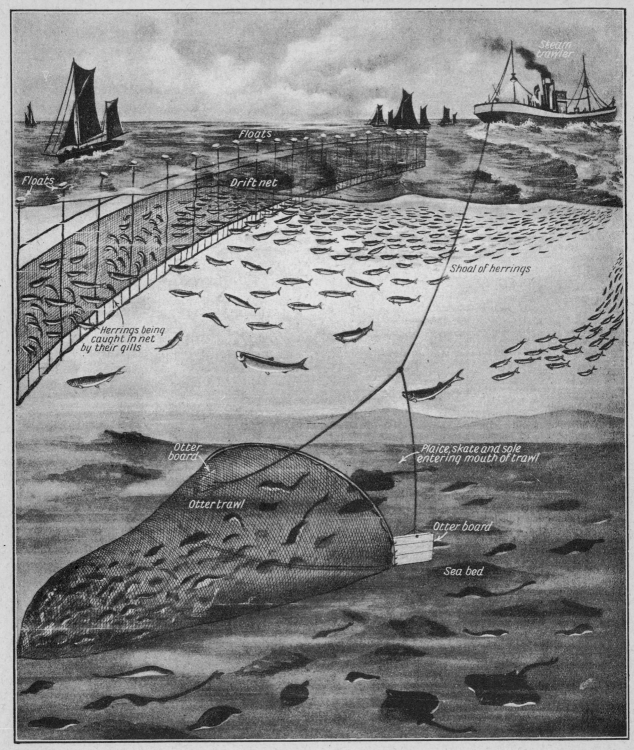

Steam trawler

Floats

Floats

Drift net

Shoal of herrings

Herrings being caught in net by their gills

Otter board

Otter trawl

Plaice, skate and sole entering mouth of trawl

Otter board

Sea bed

In this picture we see how the fish that live in the sea are caught in enormous numbers for the food of mankind. The fish that swim in the upper layers of water, such as the herring, mackerel, pilchard and sprat, are caught by means of a drift net. This is shown in the upper part of the picture. The drift net is forty feet deep and often hundreds of feet long, and it is kept floating about nine feet below the surface of the sea by means of floats. The herrings or other fish which swim in shoals are intercepted and caught by their gills in the net and are thus entrapped. Fish that live in deeper water, such as the cod, plaice, turbot, whiting, sole, haddock, brill, skate, hake, gurnard and ling, are caught by the trawl net shown in the bottom of the picture. The mouth of the net is kept open by two boards known as otter-boards, and it is dragged by the steam trawlers over the sea-bed, catching up the fish as it travels

A SALMON LEAPS TO THE TOP OF A CASCADE

The salmon is a strange fish. It is really a sea fish, but it ascends the rivers and streams at certain seasons in order to deposit its eggs on gravel, where in due course they hatch out and become young fish. After a certain time they descend to the sea, some in their first year, some in the second, and some in the third. After they have remained in the sea for a time they go back up the river. Meanwhile, the parent salmon, having spawned, go back to the sea in such a miserable condition that many die on the way. But once in the sea they soon recover and again return to the rivers. Salmon grow to a length of as much as five feet, and sometimes turn the scale at sixty pounds. In travelling up the rivers the salmon often journey for hundreds of miles, and they leap over weirs and waterfalls, jumping six feet or more at a time, like the fish in the photograph, which is jumping the Struan Falls, in Perthshire

SOME NIGHTMARES OF THE DEEP SEA

We are familiar with the forms of fish that are found near the surface of the sea, but all kinds of very unfamiliar forms are dredged up from time to time from the greater depths, where the light of the Sun never penetrates. Many of these deep-sea fish are like the creatures that appear to us in nightmares. Scientists are unable to tell us the reason for the strange forms which they assume. It can hardly be that they have developed their terrifying aspect for mere frightfulness, for where they live they cannot be seen. Some of them, however, are luminous, and shed an eerie light in the depths of the sea. In many cases, no doubt, the luminosity is for the purpose of attracting a mate. Luminous sharks are found at a depth of a mile or two. Other creatures beside fish that live in the deeper part of the ocean are luminous, such as sea worms, squids and jellyfish. The angler fishes, of which several are seen here, have a kind of rod and line which they dangle as a bait in front of their mouths in order to attract smaller creatures as prey. Many of the deep-sea fishes are also remarkable for the formidable array of teeth which they develop. Life is indeed queer in these depths

A GIANT CRAB THAT CLIMBS A TALL TREE

WE generally associate crabs with the seashore. One of the interests of a seaside holiday is to look out for crabs under stones and rocks at low tide and to study their queer habit of walking sideways.

In another part of this book we read about our common crabs, and how they are constantly changing their clothes. But all crabs do not live in the sea. There are land crabs which, though they return to the sea when they want to hatch out their young, spend most of their lives far from the sea.

The most interesting of these is known as the robber crab, a name given to it because of its remarkable habit of stealing coconuts. Perhaps we should hardly use the word " steal," for though the coconuts may have been planted by man for his own use, the robber crab does not know that he is doing anything wrong when he seizes this property, and uses it himself.

This remarkable crab lives in the islands where the Indian and Pacific Oceans join. It is a large creature, and though it has no shell its abdomen is armoured. It is really a relative of the hermit crabs of our own waters, but the robber crab's tail is not soft, and does not need protection.

Nevertheless, it has the instinct of the ordinary hermit crab, and likes to tuck its tail inside the empty shell of a coconut, or even in an old bully-beef tin. It is a remarkable example of how instincts remain, when the need and habits have changed.

The robber crab, which breathes atmospheric air, like ourselves, and not air mixed with water as its relatives that dwell in the sea do, lives upon coconut. It seizes the nuts that have fallen from the palm trees and with its heavy claws makes a hole and scoops out the white nut. Then when it has emptied the shell it makes use of this sometimes as a tail sheath.

But the robber crab does not merely appropriate the nuts that have fallen from the trees; it actually climbs the tall palms to pluck the nuts; and then when these have been dropped to the ground it climbs down again and seizes its prey.

These crabs are enormously strong, and it is said that they can break a man's arm with a nip of their powerful foreclaws, as easily as they can crack a coconut shell. Charles Darwin tells us that a specimen which was placed in a strong tin box actually made holes right through the metal and bent this down so as to be able to escape.

One of these crabs which was on show at the London Zoo used to crack the shells of Brazil nuts. That shows us how strong the claws must be, for it is not easy for ourselves to break the

A robber crab climbing a tree in search of food

shells of Brazil nuts even with nut-crackers.

In getting at the contents of a coconut the robber crab first tears away the fibre which covers the three " eyes " and then hammers with its claws until a hole is made.

It is said that sometimes when it has perforated an " eye " the crab grasps the nut firmly in its claws and breaks the shell by smashing it on a stone. This, however, is not certain.

The robber crab lives in deep burrows, which it hollows under the roots of the trees, and it carpets its home with fibre stripped from the coconuts.

The change of habit from water to land must have taken the crab a very long time, as this required a change in its breathing organs. Periodically, however, the robber crab visits the sea and there the female lays her eggs. When the young are hatched out they live for some time on the sea coast, spending much of their time in the water, but as they grow older they develop into land animals.

There are other land crabs found in both the Eastern and Western Hemispheres. Certain land crabs inhabit the West Indies, one kind being found in Jamaica. They are generally seen at a distance of two or three miles from the sea, and in the daytime remain under stones or in other sheltered situations. In the spring, the male and female crabs pair and soon afterwards they are noticed moving towards the sea. It is there, as in the case of the robber or the coconut crab, that the female lays her eggs.

When the instinct for migration seizes these land crabs nothing is allowed to hinder them. They climb over obstacles and continue on their course till they reach the water. It is a striking sight to see the migration of the land crabs. When the time comes they issue from the hollow trees and the rocky clefts in which they have been living, and assemble so rapidly that in quite a short time a great host has been mustered.

The procession of land crabs to the coast has been seen to cover an area more than a mile long, and 150 feet wide. The way is led by male crabs and the procession goes as far as possible in a straight line. The crabs climb over everything in their path, even over hedges, houses, churches, hills and cliffs.

When the young hatch out of the eggs they are miniature copies of their parents. As soon as the time comes for the crabs to moult their carapaces or shells in the late summer, they return to their burrows away from the sea, and having gone inside close up the entrances to keep out enemies. There they remain till the new shell hardens.

THE FLYING FISH AND ITS ENEMIES

THE flying fish is not a flier at all in the sense that a bird is a flier. It is really a glider. When it jumps from the water it spreads out its pectoral or breast fins, which are developed into a great size, and glides sometimes for 500 feet or more. The flight is rapid, but gets slower towards the end, though at its height the fish will race a ship going at ten miles an hour.

The fish can fly farther against the wind than when it is travelling with it or at an angle. When it takes a turning or zigzags, this is not due to any effort on the part of the fish, but is caused by the currents of air. In calm weather the line of flight is direct, and in form like the course of a projectile, but in rough weather the flying becomes undulating.

In the Atlantic and elsewhere—for the flying fish is found in many waters—the creature often falls on the decks of vessels. When the fish leaves the water it is almost invariably because an enemy is pursuing it.

The flying fish as it appears when in full flight

At such times a number of flying fish will rise from the water and begin their gliding flight, and not only do their spread fins vibrate as though they were making a real effort to fly, but their tail is often seen to work vigorously something like a screw.

In a gale, flying fish have been seen to rise as high as the top of a ship's mast. Sometimes they dart through cabin windows.

There are several species of fish that fly in this way. The flying gurnard, also found in the North Atlantic, particularly near the Sargasso Sea, is an interesting fish, for its head is protected by a heavy, thick armour, so that it is able to strike a considerable blow without hurting itself. Its side fins, when spread, form great parachutes, and the fish, being richly coloured with red, blue and yellow hues, looks like a large butterfly.

The flying fish, found in the Atlantic and other seas, has a bad time, for it has many enemies, in both water and air. It is pursued by voracious fish like the catfish and by sea mammals like the dolphin. When hunted by these creatures it leaps out of the sea and makes its flight, but the albatross and other birds are waiting to devour it there. Here we see the flying fish escaping from pursuing catfish, only to be hunted by the albatross. The flying fish is a silvery, large-eyed creature somewhat resembling a herring

THE MARVELLOUS STORY OF A FISH'S EYE

How amazed we should be if as we grew up one of our eyes were to travel round our head to the other side ! Yet this is what happens in the case of the plaice and some other flat fishes. When the fish is hatched it swims like a herring and has an eye on each side of its head. But as it grows its body starts to lean towards the left, and the right side becomes darker and darker. At the same time the head begins to twist, and as the fish grows the left eye gradually comes round, till it is on the same side as the other. These changes are to fit the fish for its future mode of life. It spends most of its time on the sea-bed, and so it is necessary for the eyes to be on the top side, in order that the fish may see above it. The darkening of the right or upper side of the fish is also a provision of Nature to protect it from enemies. With its dark skin and red spots, the fish so mingles with its surroundings as to be almost invisible from above. When, however, it is swimming an enemy looking up will hardly notice it, because the under side of its body is white like the light. The first four pictures are on a very enlarged scale compared with the later pictures of the plaice as a flat fish

AN X-RAY PHOTOGRAPH OF THE LITTLE SEA-HORSE

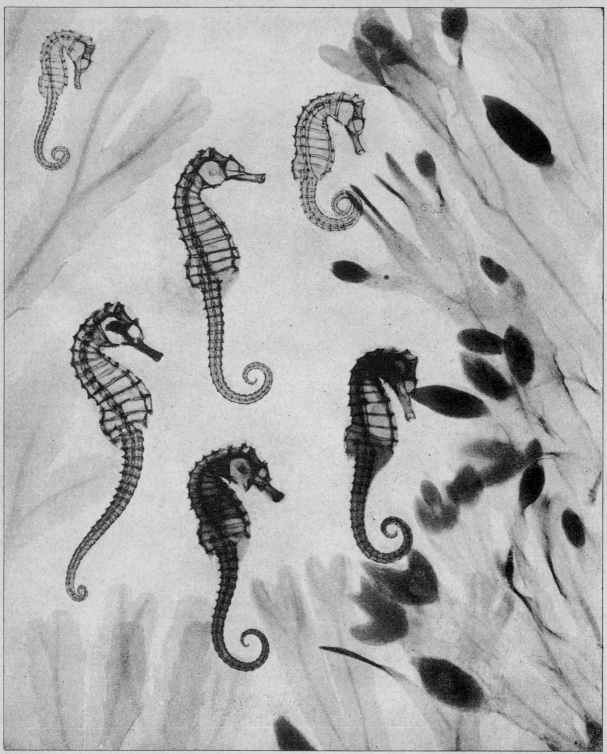

The little sea-horse, found from the Atlantic to Australia, is surely the strangest of all fish, for it looks more like a reptile or a mammal. Nevertheless, it is really a fish. It swims upright and has a flexible tail by which it clings to the stems of seaweed and coral. Sea-horses also link their tails together arm-in-arm fashion. The male has a pouch in which the eggs laid by the female are placed till they hatch out. This photograph was taken by X-rays. In the two lower fish the organs are showing. The two larger specimens above are partially dried, and show little but the bony framework, while the two top ones are completely dried specimens. There are about a score of species of sea- orse and some of these in Australian waters are remarkably like the seaweed among which they live

QUEER FISHES THAT CRAWL ON LAND

WE do not usually think of a fish as breathing atmospheric air and moving about on the land or climbing trees, yet there are fish that actually do these strange and unexpected things.

The mud-skippers of the coasts and estuaries bordering the Indo-Pacific Ocean and the shores of West Africa, for example, have such muscular development at the base of the pectoral fins, that they are able to use these for dragging themselves over the mud and for climbing.

in groups and start a procession overland, heading with unerring instinct for the nearest water.

It is said that at times the entire column of fish that is struggling through the grass halts and some of the creatures begin burrowing in the ground as though in search of water. Birds and other animals prey on them while they are thus migrating and many perish but the others eventually reach fresh supplies of water.

Another species of catfish, found in South American streams seems to like

scientist communicated to the Linnaean Society in London an account of the climbing perch declaring that it climbed trees and that he had himself captured one as it was ascending a palm tree that grew near a pond. The object of the fish in making the ascent was supposed to be to reach a small reservoir of rain water which had collected in the axils of the leaves and was full of insects.

The climbing perch forms an article of food among the poorer natives, and it is frequently sent in a dry vessel from the marshes of Jazan to Calcutta,

The Channa, a native fish of China, is able to leave the water for long periods, crawling over the dry land as shown here, by means of its fins. It generally lives in muddy water and often rises to the surface to take in air from the atmosphere. When prevented from doing this in captivity the channa dies. Of course, ordinary fish are quite unable to breathe atmospheric air

They lie on the bank of a river snapping at flies and other insects and then, when startled, jump off inland among the trees, climbing on to these and over the grass and sticks by holding on with their fins, just as if they were arms.

One of the gobies found in Texas and Mexico lives in the shallow pools left by the tide, and it is often seen crawling over the moss and weed and passing from pool to pool. When some were captured and placed in buckets a considerable distance from the water, they clambered out of the pails and crawled away to the pools.

Some of the catfishes are amphibious, like the doras of South America. In dry seasons, when the streams in which they live begin to run low and are in danger of drying up, the doras gather

to leave the water and get into the air. It is often observed floating down a river on a log of wood on which it has climbed.

But the most interesting of the fishes that move over the land is the so-called climbing perch of India, Ceylon, Malaya, and the Philippines. Its dorsal fin, that is the fin that runs along the back, has its spines much larger than the soft part, while in the anal or back fin the spines are shorter than those on the back.

It frequents estuaries, rivers and lakes which it often leaves to travel long distances over the land, dragging itself along by hitching its lower fins round the stems of grass and other herbage.

This strange habit of the fish was noticed centuries ago. Then in 1797 a

a journey of several days, which it survives, arriving at its destination alive.

As is generally known, eels find their way overland from lakes and ponds to the sea, when the urge comes to them to return to the ocean where they were born for the purpose of spawning. They are often seen crawling through the damp grass and even crossing roads. They are able to do this by a useful provision of nature. They have pockets at the sides of their heads which they fill with water and this enables them to take in air through their gills after they leave the water.

In the case of the climbing perch and other fish referred to which crawl over the land, however, the gills are modified or there are supplementary gills enabling the fish to breathe atmospheric air.

A STRANGE FISH THAT PUFFS ITSELF OUT

THE globe-fishes are among the strangest of all the creatures that live in the sea, for they can change their appearance enormously by puffing out their bodies with air, so that they are sometimes called puffers, and at other times swelling-fishes.

The different species are widely distributed, some living in the rivers of Brazil, others in the Nile and rivers of West Africa, others in the brackish water estuaries of India, and the best known of all, the porcupine globe-fish, which is about two feet in length, being found in the Atlantic and Indo-Pacific Oceans. It is generally accompanied by a smaller member of its family, called the spotted globe-fish.

In its normal state the globe-fish has a rather elongated cylindrical body, but by swallowing air it is able to blow itself out till it looks like a balloon, and in the case of the spiny globe-fish the spines stand out all round at right angles from the tightened skin as on a hedgehog.

Then a strange thing happens. The fish in this condition turns upside down and floats with its back downward. The reason for this is, of course, that its centre of gravity is changed, and it is only when upside down that it is in a state of stable equilibrium.

When inflated and inverted in this way the globe-fish is at the mercy of the waves and currents, and is driven

The globe or puffer-fish, as it appears in its normal condition

to and fro by these in a perfectly helpless condition. But no matter where it may be driven, the bristling spines keep off enemies that might devour it. Those species of globe-fish that have no protection of this kind are much more vulnerable.

It is a rather curious fact that the nearest relations of this balloon-like globe-fish are the sun-fishes, which are huge flattened creatures found in all tropical and temperate seas. They look like caricatures of fishes, having a short and greatly compressed body, with a very short tail, and all the fins joined together at the top of the body, and also at the bottom.

They have no swim bladder, and their spinal column is extremely short, having only 17 segments, of which seven belong to the tail. A sun-fish caught off Dorset in 1846 was seven and a half feet long, and another species caught off Plymouth weighed 500 pounds.

The large fins on the top and bottom of the body are the chief instruments of propulsion, and so long is the upper fin that when the creature is moving through the water the top of the fin often projects above the surface. The sun-fish feeds mostly on the larvae of other fishes, particularly those of the eel.

Another relation of the globe-fish is the sac-fish of the Indian seas. It takes its name from a sac which is formed by the dilatable skin of the abdomen. This sac can be filled with air at the will of the fish, but the lower part of the sac is a mere flap of skin that air cannot enter.

The puffer-fish blown out with air and moving through the water upside down.   These photographs were taken by Mr. Elwin R. Sanborn

A FISH THAT HOLDS ON TO SHARKS & SHIPS

Here is one of the strangest fish in the world. It is called the remora, but is more generally known as the sucking-fish because of a curious sucker which it has on top of its head and by which it attaches itself to sharks, turtles and even ships. In this way it is drawn through a much greater area of water than it could ever swim through, and so it has an opportunity of getting larger supplies of food than would otherwise be possible. It can detach itself at will. When it adheres to a ship's hull it probably supposes that this is a large shark. The people of Zanzibar, Cuba, and the Torres Straits use sucking-fishes to help them catch turtles. They tie a cord round the fish's tail and then let it loose. The fish adheres to a turtle's shell and the turtle is then drawn in and captured. The upright fish in the photograph is adhering by its sucker to the glass front of an aquarium. Other fish are lying on the pebbles at the bottom

A FIGHT BETWEEN A SHARK AND AN OCTOPUS

The photographs on this page, showing a great fight between an octopus and a tiger shark, were taken from a glass chamber let down with the photographer and camera into the sea at Samarang, in Java. They are part of a film, and here the shark is seizing the octopus

The fight was a fierce one and in the end the shark killed the octopus. These creatures are both bitter enemies of man, but they are mortal foes of one another and fight whenever they meet. It is very difficult to say which would be the more terrible to encounter

THE CUTTLEFISH AND ITS SMOKE-SCREEN

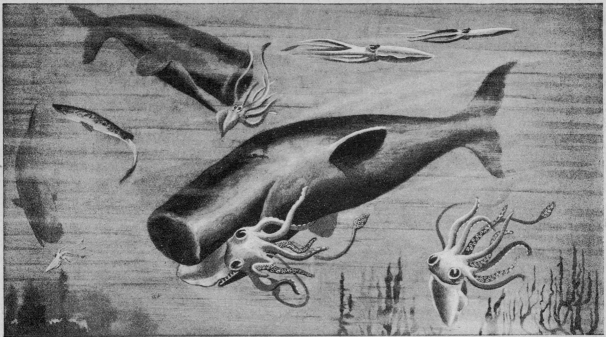

The members of the cuttlefish family are not pleasant creatures to meet in the water, for on their long feelers or tentacles they have many suckers, with which they are able to seize things and hold on tightly. They are found in all the seas of the world, even in the Antarctic, and they vary in size from a few inches to great giants with a girth of twenty feet. Indeed, Mr. Frank Bullen tells us that specimens have been seen as big as an adult sperm whale. Giants of this kind are known as squids, and have ten arms, two of them being longer than the rest. They also have two distinct fins fixed to the upper part of their body. They are believed to form a large part of the food of whales, which have actually been seen devouring them. Here a whale has just seized a squid

The octopus, though similar in general construction, has a body of a different shape from the squid's shown in the upper picture, and it has eight tentacles. The body is almost a globe in form, while the squid's tapers. The mouth of the octopus is in the centre of its tentacles, and like its relatives, it lives on fish, crabs and almost anything it can seize. An octopus is shown in the bottom right-hand corner waiting on the bed of the sea for its prey. At the top we see a cuttlefish or sepia throwing out a smoke-screen to escape from an enemy. It is the creature's form of defence against more powerful animals. It retreats backwards by squirting water from its mouth, and as it does so it ejects a dark fluid which colours the water around. From this sepia paint used to be made

A STRANGE AND UNKNOWN MONSTER OF THE SEA

Early in 1934 there was much talk about an alleged monster that had been seen in the waters of Loch Ness in Scotland. It was described as having a long neck, which it raised out of the water, and many eye-witnesses declared that they had seen it. Whatever it was, the supposed monster disappeared, but a few weeks later the animal of unknown species shown here was washed ashore near Cherbourg

The strange marine monster washed ashore near Cherbourg in March, 1934, had a long neck and a head in shape somewhat like that of a camel. There were two fins or flappers one each side of the body, and one on the back, and the middle part of the body was about 13 feet in circumference, and was partly covered with grey hairs. It was in a state of decomposition, and each time the tide came up it washed away part of the body. Here we see the creature as it appeared after a few days. Scientists were quite unable to identify it

Book 14

The ANIMAL
WONDER
BOOK

A BABY GIRAFFE WITH ITS MOTHER

A young giraffe resembles its parents from birth, being practically identical in colouring though the neck and forequarters of the young are relatively shorter. The horns, although erect and tufted like those of the adult, are soft, having no bony core. The youth of the giraffe lasts for six or seven years. It can stand about twenty minutes after it is born and is able to run freely after a day or two. In three weeks it can nibble herbage and in four months chews the cud like an adult. The beautiful marking and colouring of the giraffe are, of course, protective, and hunters bear testimony to the fact that its vivid pattern makes the animal almost invisible as it stands under the trees on which it feeds. A herd of giraffes among the red mimosas starts into life and sight only when the animals begin to move. The young giraffes are born in May or June and only a single fawn is produced at a birth. Although a full-grown giraffe can defend itself and its young by kicking out with its legs, giving a blow of such terrific force and power as to fell a lion, it relies chiefly on rapid flight to escape its enemies. Its speed and endurance in flight are great and the young keep up with their parents, thanks to their long legs

THE ELEPHANT & HIS MARVELLOUS TRUNK

The elephant is the only animal in the world that uses his nose as a hand and arm. The early ancestors of the elephants had long noses, but we do not know why this particular family of animals should develop the nose into a trunk. Perhaps one of the early members with a longer nose than usual found that it could use it for pushing or pulling down branches of trees and its descendants learned the trick. Then gradually the noses became longer and more useful, till now the trunk has become a truly wonderful limb. It has enormously powerful muscles, and in order that these may find a suitable attachment the elephant's skull has become greatly developed in size. The skull, however, must not be unduly heavy for the animal, and so the thick bone of which it is composed is honeycombed with large air spaces, so that while it is strong and big it is also light in proportion. There are many wrong ideas about what an elephant can do with its trunk. It is sometimes said that it can pick up a needle from the ground or drag a great cannon from a bog. Experts declare that it is doubtful if the former feat can be performed, and certainly the latter could not be done. Elephants dragging great weights invariably take the rope between their teeth. They never attempt to pull a heavy weight with the trunk. In carrying a log, if it is light, they hold it in the mouth as a dog does a stick, and if it is heavy and they have tusks, they rest the log on the tusks and merely steady it with the trunk, and most generally they use their heads and feet in moving great weights. Elephants are very sensitive about their trunks, and when danger threatens invariably curl them up out of harm's way, as the Indian elephant in the photograph is doing

The frogmouth of Australia, shown in this photograph, is a queer bird, and its habits recall the rhyme of Dr. Watts, " 'Tis the voice of the sluggard, I heard him complain, You've waked me too soon, I must slumber again." It seeks its food by night, not flying after the insects, but traversing the branches on which they live. It sleeps all day on gum trees unsheltered from the midday sun, and is so lethargic that it is almost impossible to rouse it. If it is actually roused it goes off to another branch and, like the fat boy in " Pickwick," falls asleep immediately. Frogmouths usually rest in pairs and if one is shot, the other one does not wake up. The bird was certainly born tired. It has the power of turning its head in every direction, even over the back, in the same way as an owl

GOING THROUGH LIFE UPSIDE DOWN

THE sloth of tropical America is a queer animal, for it spends most of its time upside down, and it even travels in the same way. It is essentially a creature of the trees, living among the branches and using the boughs as arterial roads through the forest.

It rarely if ever comes down to the ground, unless driven down by an enemy, and then it moves along with the greatest difficulty, for its front and back legs are of different lengths, and its feet with the hook-like claws, which are admirable for hanging on the branches, are not at all suited to walking or crawling.

ness being due not so much to indolence as to caution.

It never loosens its hold on one branch till it has taken a firm grip of the next. If no branch presents itself for grasping, the sloth raises its body and claws round in search of a fresh foothold. Its claws are bent into rigid hooks, admirably suited to its mode of life.

It is an animal that moves mostly by night. It will strip a tree in which it happens to be of every leaf, and only move on to another when it wants more food. It is strictly vegetarian and like all vegetarian animals needs a large quantity of food.

forms a ready prey for any assailant. Big weasels climb the trees and seize upon its throat, harpy eagles tear it loose and carry it off to their eyries, cats large and small seize upon it, and as one traveller has said, " a hungry bear collects a family of sloths as he would gather a bunch of grapes." The human dwellers in the forest do the same. The only hope of this queer animal is to remain invisible.

There are two very remarkable things about the sloth. One is that instead of having, like practically all other animals, seven bones in its neck, it has nine, and the greenish tint of its hair is due to a growth on the hairs

A three-toed sloth hanging on the branch of a tree, the normal position of this strange animal, which is regarded as a type of laziness, though if necessary it can move with great activity. It finds difficulty, however, in travelling over the ground, spending practically its whole existence in the tree-tops. The photograph is by Mr. Elwin Sanborn

We speak of a lazy person as slothful, which means that he is very slow in his movements, and the sloth is given its name for the same reason.

But it can, if necessary, travel with great speed through the forest, moving from branch to branch and making use of the swaying of the boughs to cross gaps between the trees. Unless there is some reason, however, for quick movement, even in the tree it moves lazily from branch to branch, its slow-

By day it sleeps rolled up into a ball with the head tucked between the arms, when it has a striking resemblance to the lichen-clad knots of the trees.

Sloths are found generally in pairs, or in small family parties, and they are perfectly harmless. They rarely if ever drink water, getting all the moisture they need from the young shoots and fruits of trees on which they feed.

The sloth has no means of defence, and when it hangs on a leafless bough

of microscopic plants, which take root in the crevices of the surface of the hairs, and flourish there as long as the animal lives.

There are two kinds of sloth, one known as the two-toed and the other as the three-toed. Each has a different kind of hair, and the hairs support different species of plants. In habits and general behaviour, however, the two species are very much alike. They are near relatives of the ant-eaters.

A BIRD THAT CAN KICK LIKE A HORSE

THE OSTRICH AND ITS WONDERFUL APPETITE

The old story that the ostrich is a very stupid bird and that when pursued it buries its head in the sand or in a bush, believing that because it cannot see it cannot be seen, is only a traveller's yarn. Those who have studied the ostrich tell us that it is quite as intelligent as any other bird. If an enemy approaches its nest or pursues the mother bird and young, the cock will try to lead the foe off in a wrong direction by running in front of him or pretending to be wounded. Altogether, the ostrich is a very remarkable bird, as we read here

THE biggest bird in the world is the ostrich, and a very marvellous creature it is. A full-size male bird stands eight feet high, weighs three or four hundredweights, and can give a kick which will kill a man.

The ostrich has always been a very useful bird to mankind. In the southern part of Africa, which is its chief home, its huge eggs, weighing three or four pounds each, yield an excellent and nourishing food supply. Magnificent feathers from the wings and tail have provided not only decoration, but dress for the natives of Africa, and from time to time ostrich feathers have become fashionable in civilized countries. At such times the price rises to as much as two or three dollars a feather, and the birds themselves may realize as much as $1000.

There are several species of ostrich, one kind living in North Africa, Syria and Mesopotamia, and another kind in Somaliland, but the best known species is that found in South Africa, particularly in the Kalahari Desert, and in the country of the Matabele and Mashona peoples.

In desert country covered with patches of bush the ostrich can hide and yet watch for its enemies without being seen, for its long bare neck and small flat head rising above the bushes are difficult to discern at a distance.

A Runner Without Equal

The ostrich cannot fly, but as a runner it has no equal, and its outspread wings help its speed, acting in somewhat the same way as aeroplane wings. It can outstrip the fastest antelope or horse, and often reaches a speed of 26 miles an hour, but it has a foolish habit of running in a circle, so that it does not escape the hunter. It can live for long without water, but in the hot season if it is near a lake or the sea it will often bathe.

Perhaps the most extraordinary thing about the ostrich is its appetite. It is really omnivorous, and its food consists of small mammals, birds, snakes, lizards, insects, grass, leaves, fruits and seeds. But it does not stop at these things. It will swallow keys, nails, coins, buttons, and other metal objects, glass, stones, and in fact anything, but it is not always able to digest such strange fare, and there are several cases on record of ostriches dying after swallowing pieces of glass.

The Missing Snuff Box

One ostrich when dissected was found to have nearly a peck of stones inside its body, most of them being worn as smooth as if polished by a skilled lapidary. A consul at Tripoli missed a silver snuff box of considerable size and value, and many people were suspected of having stolen it. An

An ostrich resting on its powerful legs, one kick from which could kill a man

ostrich which was kept in the grounds was, a little later, shipped to Europe, but died during the voyage. It was opened to ascertain the cause of death, and in the body were found nails, keys, pieces of iron and copper, part of a lantern, and the missing snuff box, the chasing and sharp edges of which had been worn completely smooth.

The male birds often make a noise like the roaring of a lion, and at other times, particularly in the morning, low like an ox. When they are feeding, however, they utter a kind of hissing chuckle, but the young birds are silent.

When the pairing season comes, the male bird will associate with several hens, all of which lay their eggs in a single nest, and then the cock does most of the incubating. He sits on the nest all night, so as to keep off jackals that would steal the eggs, and even in the daytime he covers the eggs for hours, though the female birds then take their turns. In the daytime the birds leave the nest altogether for considerable periods, covering the eggs with sand, and they are kept from getting addled by the Sun's heat.

In Somaliland the natives hunt the ostrich on camels, and at other times catch the huge birds by digging pitfalls. The bushmen of South Africa, on the other hand, dress up in ostrich skins and approach the birds so as to shoot poisoned arrows at them.

Plucking the Feathers

When ostrich feathers were very fashionable in Europe and America, a number of ostrich farms were started in South Africa, and some of the birds were taken to the United States in 1882, and ostrich farms started in California.

It is only the male bird that produces the beautiful feathers that are so much admired. When these are at their best the bird is placed in a wooden case with his neck projecting through a hole, and a hood like a stocking is put over his head. Then the feathers are clipped. The bird suffers no pain, as no blood is drawn and no nerve is touched.

The ostrich's chief means of defence is its powerful legs, which can give a kick that will disable a fierce quadruped, but when fighting its own species it often uses its beak as well as its legs.

The Romans were very fond of ostrich flesh, and the Emperor Heliogabalus once had 600 cooked and served at a supper he gave. A notable Roman glutton named Firmius is said to have devoured an entire ostrich at one meal.

SPRING-HEELED JACKS OF AUSTRALIA

There are over fifty different kinds of kangaroos, large and small, and they are all great jumpers. Although they are by nature furnished with four legs, they use only the two hind ones as organs of progression. The kangaroo springs from the ground in an erect position, and propelled by its powerful hind legs and balanced by its tail, with its forearms held towards the chest, it sets off hopping at an astonishing pace, clearing very often thirty feet at each spring. It is also a good jumper, and when pursued can easily clear low fences

A LIVING DRAGON LOOKS OUT OF ITS LAIR

This striking picture shows one of the land iguanas of the Galapagos Islands. It is a stoutly built lizard with a comparatively small head and the body has a spiny crest along the back. The limbs end in short toes with sharp claws. The tail is longer than the head and body together, and the whole animal is about three feet long and weighs from ten to fifteen pounds. In this photograph the iguana certainly looks like one of the prehistoric monsters of a past age. There is really nothing by which we can judge its size. The whole picture is indeed an interesting example of relativity. If a boy or girl had been taken in the photograph by the side of the iguana, then the animal would have appeared its true size. These iguanas live in burrows and are very sluggish in their movements. At every few steps they stop for a minute or two and doze with closed eyes. They feed by day on the succulent cactus of their native haunts, and on leaves of trees, climbing the trees for the purpose. The females lay large eggs. People in the Galapagos Islands eat their flesh

THE INDOLENT BEAR AND ITS HABITS

BEARS are always popular animals in zoos and menageries, partly because of the very human way in which they walk upright on their hind legs, and partly because of their queer and amusing antics. They always seem such friendly animals, although, of course, in the wilds an angry bear is a formidable creature.

There are many kinds of bears, the polar bear and the brown bear being perhaps the most familiar. Then there is the grizzly, a large, massive animal that is a native of the western United States and north-west Canada, the black bear of North America, and another species of black bear in Asia, found in the Himalayas and in Japan. Besides these there are various lesser varieties, like the sun bear, found from Assam to Borneo, and the spectacled bear of the Andes.

Bears are omnivorous; little comes amiss to them in the way of food, but they are particularly fond of honey, and rob the wild bees' nests. The grizzly and polar bear, however, are largely carnivorous.

Farm Raiders

All the species of bears found in northern lands are powerful and courageous animals, but are rather indolent, and this is fortunate for the smaller beasts, which often escape through the bears laziness in pursuit. In the neighbourhood of human habitations bears often make raids upon farms and carry off colts, calves, lambs and pigs. They will climb the fence, seize the animal and then hurry off with it.

When in great haste a bear can gallop as fast as a pony, but being so heavy he cannot keep up the pace for long, and usually he is seen travelling in a rapid, shuffling walk, the tracks he leaves being very much like those made by men.

A bear will tear open the home of a beaver or musk rat and devour the tenant, unless it has been fortunate enough to get away. Alaskan bears pursue the ground squirrels in spring. They try to catch the little creatures by a sudden pounce, but are not often successful in this; and when the squirrel dodges and enters a burrow the bear immediately begins to attack, generally using his left paw and watching the hole closely all the time.

Sometimes the squirrel manages to run out and escape between the legs of the bear. The bear then makes for another hole, and here the same tactics are followed, but generally the bear succeeds in the end.

The bear is also a good fisherman, and often wades into large rivers at night to catch fish, going in up to the neck and moving slowly with the current. It is generally the she-bear that does the fishing, while her cubs wait on the bank. She keeps her arms at her sides with her hands spread ready, and when she feels a salmon or other fish come against her body she clutches it with her claws, and throws it on to the bank for the waiting cubs.

After the young are well supplied the bear puts the next fish into her own mouth, and wades ashore to eat it. When fishing in shallow water, however,

A couple of young Alaskan bears snapshotted while in an argument

the bear generally walks on all fours, and when she sees a fish, strikes it on the head. This is the method of the bears of Alaska and Kamchatka.

The black bear of the American woods has been seen fishing in a different way. A naturalist tells us how he came suddenly upon a bear in a thick swamp, lying upon a large hollow log across a brook. The animal fished in this wise:

"There was a large hole through the log on which he lay, and he thrust his forearm through the hole and held his open paw in the water and waited for the fish to gather around and into it, and when filled he clutched his fist and brought up a handful of fish, and sat and ate them with great gusto; then down with the paw again, and so on.

"The brook was fairly alive with little trout and red-sided suckers and some black suckers. He did not eat their heads. There was quite a pile of them on the log. I suppose the oil in his paw attracted the fish and baited them even better than a fly hook, and his toenails were his hooks, and sharp ones, too, and once grabbed the fish were sure to stay."

The bear is very fond of insects, which form a prominent part of his food supply. Those insects that live in colonies and have large nests stored with grubs are particularly sought after, and all kinds of bears, except the polar bear, spend a good deal of their time in tearing up decayed logs and tree stumps in search of the larvae which occupy the crevices. Bears also dig out the ants' nests.

When the bear attacks a bees' nest the insects swarm over the animal's body, sting him and creep into his ears and eyes and mouth, till often he rolls about in pain. But he generally remains at the feast till satisfied and then ambles off to lick himself.

Strong Claws

The greatest of all the insect-hunting bears is the Indian sloth bear, often called the honey bear. Its favourite food is the termites or white ants. Even the hardest soil can be dug up by the claws, three or four inches long, of this remarkable excavator. The claws are as effective as a pickaxe. The sloth bear has large powers of suction and having made a hole in the white ants' nest, is able to draw out large quantities of the insects by suction. The sucking process can be heard 600 feet or more away.

In summer, however, most bears are vegetarians, living on fruits of various kinds, roots, bark, lichens and tender shoots of plants. They also like nuts and grapes. The stomach of an Alaskan black bear which was shot was found packed full of crowberries.

The grizzly when roused is a very formidable animal, and can kill a man by one blow of his paw. He has even been known to break the neck of a bison with one stroke. There is no truth in the popular idea that a bear hugs his victim to death.

Bears hibernate in the winter, but do not become torpid.

A CREATURE WHICH GROWS ITS OWN HOME

THE story of the development of the tortoise is a very strange one. Here is an animal which moves about very slowly and carries on its back a house into which it can retire when danger threatens

In far-back times the tortoise did not have a shell or carapace on its back, but it started to develop an armour-plated skin made up of bony nodules covered with a sheath of horn, and as this, in the course of time, increased in weight and size, it hindered the movements of the animal's backbone.

The result was that the muscles of the back, having less and less work to do, dwindled away, and the back shell gradually became lowered on to the ribs and spine till at last shell and ribs became welded together, forming the shell of the tortoise as we know it to-day.

The bony plates have become beautifully linked with the ribs, but down the middle of the shell, if we examine a tortoise, we can still see the tops of the spines of the backbone The tortoise.

having developed this heavy armour for protection, something had to be sacrificed, and it was speed that went.

A tortoise in a garden making its first meal of lettuce leaves after waking from its long winter sleep

The tortoise now crawls about very slowly and deliberately, carrying the heavy carapace, which is a combined house and skeleton, with it.

There are small tortoises like the Greek tortoise of Mediterranean countries, which are often kept in gardens, and there are giants like those of the Galapagos Islands, which sometimes weigh over 600 pounds and are more than four feet long. These live for several centuries.

The European tortoise is an interesting animal to keep as a pet. People with no knowledge of natural history often buy specimens to destroy black beetles or other insects, but, of course, the tortoise is a strict vegetarian. It loves water, and in warm weather if placed under a running tap will put out its neck in different directions to get well bathed. It hibernates during the winter, burying itself just under the ground, often in a flower-bed, and appears again next year when the weather begins to get warm. It is very hungry after its sleep.

A giant tortoise in a zoo which is big enough and strong enough for a boy or girl to ride on its back. In its native haunts this animal, which lives for several centuries, grows much bigger than the specimen in the picture, often reaching four feet

THE DESTRUCTIVE DOG OF AUSTRALIA

Our domesticated dogs are descended from wolves or jackals, or possibly both, but there are also breeds of wild dogs, and one of these is the dingo, of Australia, two specimens of which are shown here. This animal is believed to have originated from some of the domesticated dogs of Asia, introduced into the island-continent by man. That this is the origin of the dingo is supported by the fact that a half-wild, dingo-like dog is found in Java, and the dingo may have made its way to Australia via south-eastern Asia. It is probably a near relation of the Indian pariah dog. It is smaller than a wolf, has long legs and a long bushy tail, with well-developed ears. In colour it varies from red to black, with greyish under-fur. The end of the tail and sometimes the feet are often nearly white. The dingo is a great enemy of the sheep farmer, killing and mangling far more sheep than it eats. It is also destructive to poultry, and man has to wage a fierce war of extermination against it in order to save his stocks

KING PENGUINS GOING FOR A STROLL

There are seventeen different kinds of penguins and some of them are quite small, but the giants of the family are the King and Emperor penguins of the Antarctic. In this picture we see two King penguins in their customary attitude. They are most amusing birds, for as they strut along in an upright position they look just like rather pompous old gentlemen on their dignity. Their expressions and raised beaks help the illusion. In their native haunts King penguins live on small crustaceans, soft-bodied molluscs, and particularly young cuttle-fish. In captivity, however, they live on fish, but they will never pick up a fish from the ground or even take it from the water, so in zoos they always have to be hand fed by the keepers. One penguin will eat sixty fish in a single day

THE APE THAT MOST RESEMBLES MAN

The chimpanzee, one of the man-like apes whose home is in the forests of Central Africa, has such amusing and attractive ways that one cannot help feeling an affection for it. It is certainly one of the most popular of all the inmates of the   Zoo; but, unfortunately, like the other man-like apes, it is slowly disappearing from the world. Here are many interesting facts about this intelligent and very human animal

SCIENTISTS tell us that of all the man-like apes, the chimpanzee is nearest to man in bodily structure. Certainly in its appearance and ways it is most human. Its face has quite a kindly and human expression, it is affectionate to its kind, and it can be taught easily to do all manner of things that human beings do. It will sit at a table and eat and drink like a child, it loves fun and play and when dressed in human garb, suggests its kinship with ourselves.

The chimpanzee is a social animal, and in the wild state lives in family parties numbering from twelve to forty. It is sad to think that as man encroaches upon the territory occupied by these interesting apes their numbers get fewer and fewer, and as Arthur Keith has said, when the great African forest belt disappears the chimpanzee will go with it. At the present time it is estimated that the chimpanzee population of Africa, its native home, does not exceed 150,000.

Men of science place the chimpanzee first in order of intelligence among the man-like apes, although its brain is less in size than those of the orang-utan and gorilla. At its birth the chimpanzee is only about one-third the weight of a human baby. Although the human baby does not get its first teeth till it is six months old or more, the baby chimpanzee begins to cut its teeth at two months, and has all its milk teeth when it is a year old.

Unlike the human baby, the chimpanzee can begin to look after itself at the age of two years, and it is quite grown up when it is fourteen. It then weighs about 100 to 150 pounds, resembling man in this respect, but its body is longer and its lower limbs shorter. It is not often that a chimpanzee is more than four feet eight inches high. Arthur Keith tells us

that in general wear of the body a chimpanzee is as old in its fortieth year as a man in his seventieth.

The chimpanzee has been known in Europe for more than four centuries, and it is among the most popular of all animals in zoological gardens. It requires great attention to keep it healthy, but nowadays zoos,   are able by scientific treatment, to keep the animals alive for years

Two young chimpanzees at the   Zoo looking at their visitors

The hands and feet of the chimpanzee are more slender than those of the gorilla, and as in the case of man, the middle finger is longer than any of the others.

Chimpanzees inhabit Western and Central Equatorial Africa, and range over a large extent of country. They are forest dwellers, though in one district they are found in the moun-

tains. In the wild state they live upon fruits, and are strictly vegetarian, but in captivity they take quite kindly to a mixed diet in which animal food has an essential part.

In their native home the parties of chimpanzees are always on the move in order to find fresh feeding grounds. They make a loud cry which can be heard sounding through the forests at all hours of the day and night. Their voice travels a great distance, and many chimpanzees will be calling at one time. This ape remains a good deal on the ground, but it climbs trees for the sake of obtaining the fruits or to rest. It builds rough nests high up in the trees, where the females and young sleep, while the male takes up a position beneath the shelter so as to protect its family.

Scientists declare that the intelligence of many chimpanzees is equal to that of a child a few months before emerging from the period of infancy, and is thus far higher than that of any other mammal except man.

The chimpanzee, when moving about, walks on all fours. It is covered with hair, the prevailing colour of which is black.

When necessary the chimpanzee can be quite fierce, and it is a powerful animal. It generally flees at the sight of man, but if its retreat is cut off it will turn and attack fiercely, when it is an exceedingly awkward customer to deal with. Dr. Livingstone says that the chimpanzee kills the leopard occasionally by seizing both paws and biting them. The lion, however, kills the chimpanzee at once, but does not eat it.

When the chimpanzee travels on all-fours it generally supports itself on the backs of its closed fingers and not on the palms of its hands. It also goes sometimes on the soles of its feet and sometimes on its closed toes.

THE UGLIEST OF ALL THE ANIMALS

It is not without some justification that the wart-hog of South and East Africa and Abyssinia has been called the ugliest of all animals. It has an enormous head with the lower part of the face very broad and flat, and has a huge warty growth below each eye and two other big warts between the eyes and tusks. These tusks complete the hideous appearance of the animal and are found in both male and female. Unlike what is the case in other pigs the tusks of the upper jaw are much longer than those of the lower. The wart-hog often occupies the deserted burrow of an aard-vark and when it emerges it turns a somersault on to the back of the mound and travellers standing there for safety have suddenly had their legs ripped open by the wart-hog's tusks. The upper tusks which curve upward and inward are often eight or nine inches long. Samuel Baker tells us that when the wart-hog becomes excited it cocks a long thin tail, with bristles upon either side, like that of an elephant. This is carried straight in the air, as stiff as a stick, which gives the animal a ridiculous appearance

THE CURIOUS CAMEL OF SOUTH AMERICA

The llama—not to be misspelt lama, which means a Tibetan Buddhist priest—is the camel of South America.   It is smaller and lighter in build than its relations the Old World camels, and has no hump. The llama can live only in cold or temperate regions, and while in Patagonia it thrives on the plains, farther north it lives high up in the Andes.   Near the equator it is found three miles above sea level. There are two wild breeds of llama, the larger known as the guanaco and the smaller as the vicuna.   The domesticated llama, bred as a beast of burden like the horse and ass, is a guanaco.   The llama has a nasty habit, when annoyed, of spitting at people

THE ANIMAL THE WORLD NEARLY LOST

One of the most astonishing romances of animal life is the story of the American bison.   It roamed the plains of North America in millions, but owing to senseless slaughter it was almost exterminated.   Then a few pairs were protected in reservations, and these have now multiplied till there are large herds in special National parks in both the United States and Canada.   As late as 1871 a herd was seen in Arkansas 25 miles wide and 50 miles long.   It was estimated to contain four million animals.   While the European bison is a denizen of the forest, the American bison is a grazing animal of the plains.   Here we see a cow bison with her calf.   The bulls often weigh a ton

Book 15

The MIRACULOUS
MACHINE CALLED
MAN

THE ACTUAL VALUE OF A GREAT MAN

Enough lime to whitewash a henhouse

Enough magnesium for two or three flashlight photographs

Ten gallons of water

SULPHUR TABLETS

Sufficient sulphur for a packet of sulphur tablets

Enough iron to make one nail

Enough fat to make 7 bars of soap

SAFETY MATCHES

Enough phosphorus to tip the matches in 3 dozen boxes

Enough sugar to sweeten the tea at a mothers meeting

Galileo — Napoleon — Darwin — Shakespeare — Newton — Edison

AMMONIA

Enough ammonia to carry out the spring cleaning in a house

SALT

Sufficient salt to cook a dinner

Who can estimate the value of such men as William Shakespeare, Charles Darwin and Thomas Alva Edison? Their services to the world have been so great that it would be impossible to give them any money value. Their price is above rubies. Yet there is a sense in which the money value of any man or woman or child can be reckoned up with fair accuracy. If we consider a person only from a material point of view, that is, the amount of matter in his body, the part of him that we can handle and see, then the worth of even a Shakespeare or a Napoleon is very small indeed. A scientist has with some humour reckoned up the value of a full-grown man's body and above we see what it consists of. It makes no difference whether the man is a genius like the men shown in the middle of the picture, or a dullard. Indeed, often an ignorant and foolish person may be worth more in this sense than a genius, for his body may be very big and stout, so that there is more material in it. Of course our bodies, like everything else in the world, are made up of combinations of elementary substances like oxygen and hydrogen and carbon and nitrogen and phosphorus and sulphur, with a few metals like calcium and iron. It is interesting to know how little the material of our bodies is worth, but, at the same time, we must remember the great value of the human body as a channel for expressing the wonders of the mind

WHAT HAPPENS WHEN YOU TOUCH SOMETHING HOT

Message passing from association area to arm area

Arm area sending message telling muscles to remove finger from hot stove

Message from finger received at sensory area of brain and passed to association area

Message from finger passing up arm nerve to brain

Burning sensation in finger tip causes nerve to send a message to the brain

If by chance you touch something hot, such for example as the top of a stove, you very soon move your finger from the hot place. You do not have to think out the matter ; the whole process is almost instantaneous. In this picture we are shown in diagram form exactly what happens. When the nerves of your finger-tip experience the sensation of burning, they send a message up the nerves of your arm to the part of the brain where such sensations are understood. A message passes thence to an association centre in the brain, which connects the burning sensation with the stove and the finger-tip, and from there a message goes on to that part of the motor area of the brain which deals with the arm, and a message is instantly sent down the nerves of the arm and hand, telling the muscles to take the finger away from the place of danger. All this happens in the fraction of a second, much quicker than would be possible if we had to reason out the matter consciously. The same kind of thing occurs if any other part of the body feels the sensation of pain from outside, and even when danger threatens, as when something approaches our eye, we instantaneously draw away

WHAT HAPPENS WHEN WE TASTE THINGS

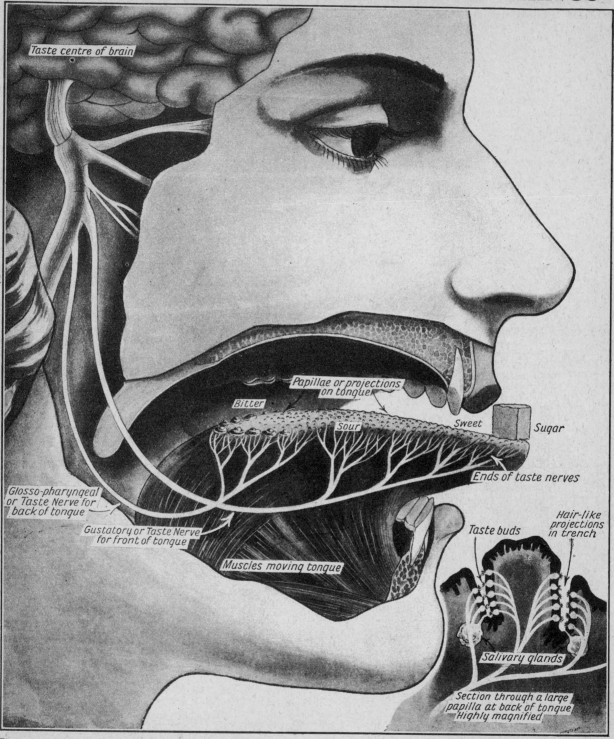

Taste centre of brain

Papillae or projections on tongue

Bitter

Sour

Sweet

Sugar

Ends of taste nerves

Glosso-pharyngeal or Taste Nerve for back of tongue

Gustatory or Taste Nerve for front of tongue

Muscles moving tongue

Hair-like projections in trench

Taste buds

Salivary glands

Section through a large papilla at back of tongue Highly magnified

The sense of taste is both useful and pleasant. In this picture we see what happens when we taste things. It is by means of the wet membrane or lining of our tongue and the back part of the palate, or roof of the mouth, that we get the sensation of taste, and this is carried by nerves to the taste centre of the brain. It is the back part of the tongue especially which is used in tasting. The tongue is covered with little projections called papillae, and at the back of the tongue some of these are large, each being surrounded by a groove or trench. In these trenches and at the sides of smaller papillae there are what are known as taste buds, each consisting of a cluster of cells. The cells in the centre of the bud have tiny hair-like projections, and when we take anything into our mouth these hair-like projections are stimulated, and send their message through the nerve to the brain. The ends of the taste nerves are in the papillae. Sweetness is tasted mostly by the tip of the tongue, bitterness by the back, and sourness by the sides

WHAT HAPPENS WHEN WE SMELL A ROSE

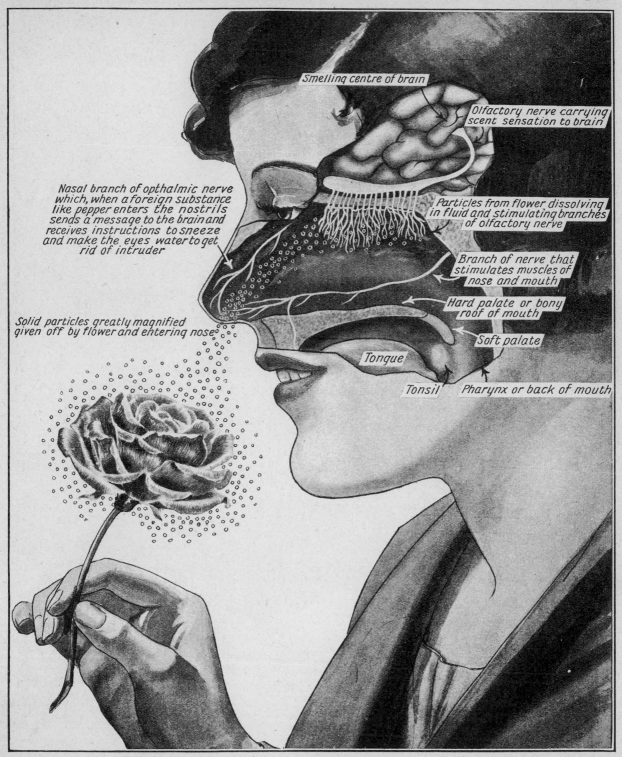

Smelling centre of brain

Olfactory nerve carrying scent sensation to brain

Nasal branch of opthalmic nerve which, when a foreign substance like pepper enters the nostrils sends a message to the brain and receives instructions to sneeze and make the eyes water to get rid of intruder

Particles from flower dissolving in fluid and stimulating branches of olfactory nerve

Branch of nerve that stimulates muscles of nose and mouth

Hard palate or bony roof of mouth

Solid particles greatly magnified given off by flower and entering nose

Soft palate

Tongue

Tonsil

Pharynx or back of mouth

We all love to smell a rose or other sweet-scented flower, but not many people know exactly how it is we are able to smell. The thing we smell gives off tiny particles, generally in the solid state, but far too small to be seen or felt. These enter our nostrils and pass into the upper part of our noses, where alone the smelling is done. They have to be dissolved in a fluid before the olfactory, or smell, nerve can be excited and send a message to the smelling centre of the brain. That is why if the upper part of our nose becomes dry we cannot smell. When we have a cold, too, our noses become stopped, and we cannot smell because the particles are unable to reach the upper nose. The nerves in the lower part of the nose, when stimulated as by pepper, make us sneeze, to expel the offending substance.

INSIDE OUR EAR AND INSIDE A TELEPHONE

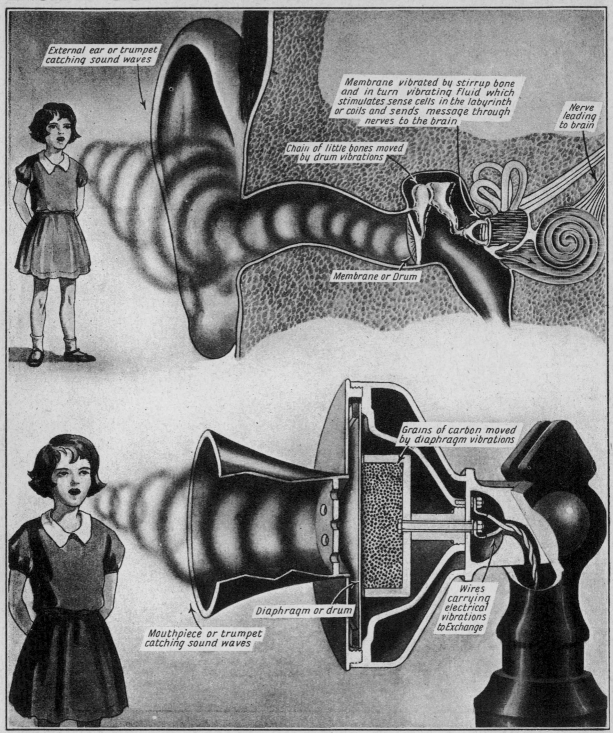

External ear or trumpet catching sound waves

Membrane vibrated by stirrup bone and in turn vibrating fluid which stimulates sense cells in the labyrinth or coils and sends message through nerves to the brain

Nerve leading to brain

Chain of little bones moved by drum vibrations

Membrane or Drum

Grains of carbon moved by diaphragm vibrations

Diaphragm or drum

Mouthpiece or trumpet catching sound waves

Wires carrying electrical vibrations to Exchange

When someone sings or speaks, the sounds set up waves in the air. These enter our outer ear, pass down a channel or canal, and strike upon a membrane called the drum. This vibrates and sets moving a chain of three little bones, called from their shape the hammer, the anvil and the stirrup. The last named vibrates another membrane, which in turn vibrates a fluid, and the motion is passed on till it stimulates the nerve of hearing, and a message is sent to the hearing centre of the brain, which distinguishes different kinds of sound. It is not really the ear that hears, but the mind of man. The telephone is very similar to the human ear. Sound waves enter the mouthpiece, vibrate a diaphragm, which sets a number of grains of carbon moving, thereby affecting an electrical current passing through them, and the vibrations are transmitted by the current through wires to a receiving instrument at the other end, where they are translated back into sound and we hear them as we hold the receiver to our ear

THE EYE OF OUR BODY AND THE EYE OF A CAMERA

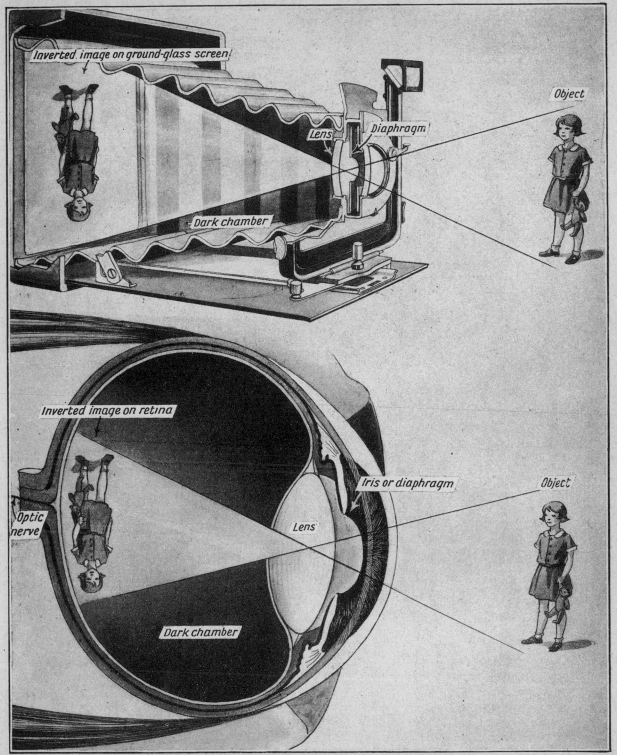

Inverted image on ground-glass screen

Lens

Diaphragm

Object

Dark chamber

Inverted image on retina

Optic nerve

Iris or diaphragm

Object

Lens

Dark chamber

There is a remarkable resemblance between the way a picture is recorded in a camera and the way it is recorded on the retina or curtain of the eye. The camera and the eye have each a lens with a diaphragm, or kind of shutter, in front. An opening in the shutter can be made larger or smaller according to the amount of light available. In the camera this has to be worked by the operator, but in the eye it is automatic. Rays of light pass from an object through the lens as shown here, so that an inverted image appears on the screen at the back. When the inverted picture falls on the retina of the eye this stimulates the optic nerve and sends a message to the seeing part of the brain, and we get the sensation of sight. Our eyes see everything upside down, but our brains reverse the picture

THE WONDERFUL WAY THE BRAIN WORKS

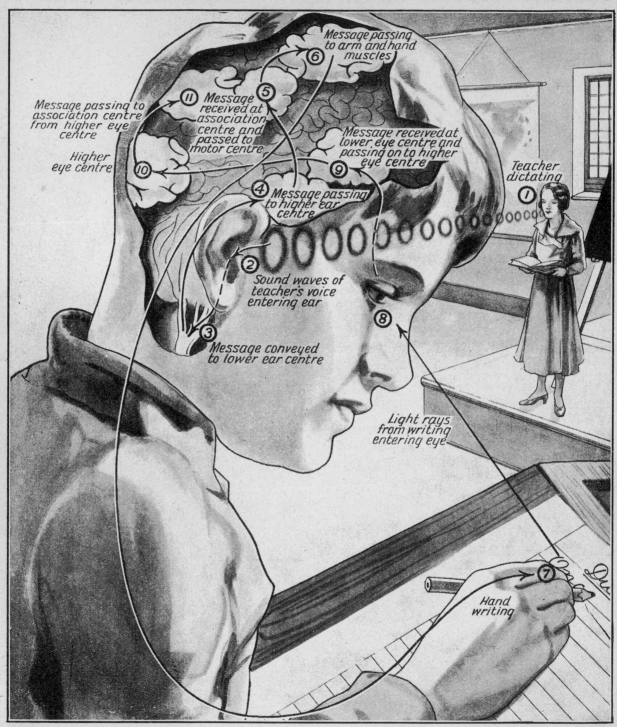

In this picture diagram we get an idea of the wonderful way in which our brain does the work that is required of it. Not only the brain itself but the nerves by which it receives messages and through which it transmits orders to the muscles, work practically instantaneously. Here a school teacher is dictating to a class, and we see how the sound waves from her mouth enter the ear of the scholar and send a message to the lower ear centre, which receives the impression of the sounds. Thence the message passes to the higher ear centre, which interprets the sounds and sends a message to an association centre and then on to a motor centre, from which a message is sent along a nerve to the arm and hand muscles, ordering them to write the words that have been dictated. Light rays from the writing enter the scholar's eye, and a message is received at the lower eye centre of the brain, recognising the marks on the paper. Thence a message goes to the higher eye centre, which interprets the meaning of the words seen, and then passes to the association centre, which links up what is heard and what is seen

THE WORK OF DIFFERENT PARTS OF THE BRAIN

The human brain is a very complex piece of machinery, and different parts of it are used for different purposes. Our nerves carry messages to the brain from different parts of the body, and messages are sent from the brain to eye, ear, arm, leg, and other organs, telling them what to do. But the nerves for the different functions lead to different parts of the brain. For example, the front of the brain deals with speech, whereas the back deals with seeing. When a well-known footballer fell on the field during a game and was kicked by accident on the back of his head, he was blind for several days. The reason can be seen quite clearly from this picture, for it was the seeing part of his brain that was damaged and so upset his sight for the time being

WHAT YOUR BODY LOOKS LIKE INSIDE

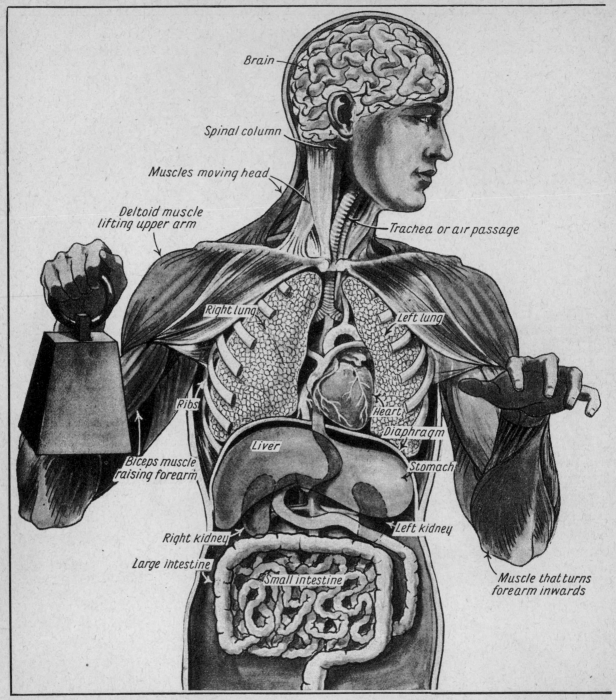

Brain

Spinal column

Muscles moving head

Deltoid muscle
lifting upper arm

Trachea or air passage

Right lung

Left lung

Heart

Ribs

Diaphragm

Liver

Stomach

Biceps muscle
raising forearm

Left kidney

Right kidney

Muscle that turns
forearm inwards

Large intestine

Small intestine

The human body is the most wonderful thing in the universe. It is the most efficient of all machines, and unless it is damaged or spoilt by accident or misuse it goes on doing its work perfectly day after day, till at last, like all material things, it becomes worn out. But the machinery of the human body is extraordinarily delicate, and the more we know about our body and realise this fact, the more careful we shall be to see that it is not misused in any way by wrong living. We are often told that the heart which drives the life-giving blood through our bodies is an engine and pump, and that the stomach is a furnace. But when we look at a chart like this one showing the organs, it is rather difficult to realise that we are looking at a furnace, a pump, and other machinery. The picture-diagram on the opposite page will make the matter clear and vivid to our imaginations. By comparing the two pictures we shall see that it is no mere fancy or exaggeration to describe the human body as a great and wonderful factory. Perhaps the most marvellous thing about our body is the perfect way in which its various parts all work together. If any part gets out of order and ceases to function, as, for example, if we eat unsuitable food, thereby supplying wrong fuel to the furnace, or if we breathe bad air, so that the furnace cannot get sufficient oxygen for combustion of the fuel, then the whole factory becomes disorganised, and we say we are ill. We notice how the whole body is built round the bones of the skeleton in the same way as a factory is built on a skeleton of girders

THE HUMAN BODY SHOWN AS A FACTORY

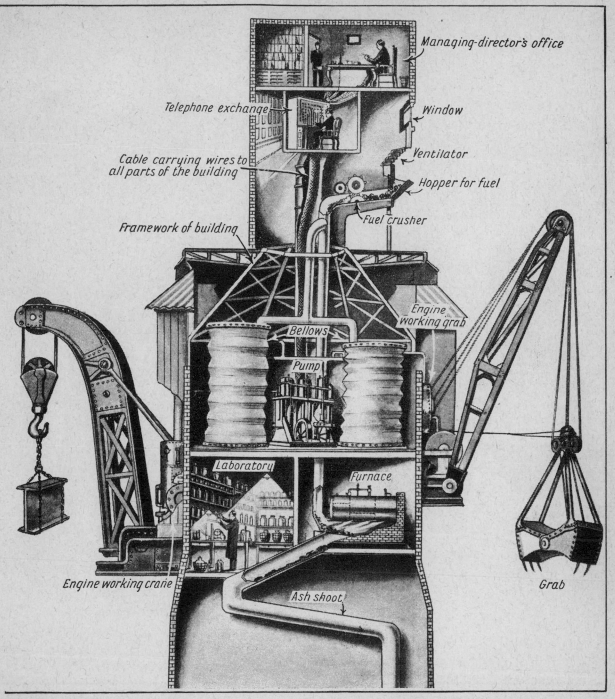

Managing-director's office

Telephone exchange

Window

Ventilator

Cable carrying wires to all parts of the building

Hopper for fuel

Fuel crusher

Framework of building

Engine working grab

Bellows

Pump

Laboratory

Furnace

Engine working crane

Ash shoot

Grab

In this picture, which corresponds to the form of the body, we see the functions of the various parts and how closely they correspond to the parts of a factory. A factory would be useless without some directing head, and our skull is like the managing director's office, for it is from the brain inside that all the work of the human factory is directed. There must be a telephone exchange so that messages can be sent to the right departments, and this we get in the lower part of the brain and the spinal column. Our eyes are like the windows of the office. Then the factory must be properly ventilated, and fresh air is taken in from outside through openings, as our body does through nose and mouth. To keep the machinery of the factory going there must be a furnace and engine, and so in our body the stomach and intestines form a furnace that must be supplied regularly with suitable fuel. In a factory the fuel is shot through a hopper and directed to the furnace, the coal being crushed to a suitable size. In the human body food, which is the fuel, is taken in through the mouth, broken up by the teeth, and then passes to the stomach, the unconsumed ash being disposed of. The lungs are the bellows that supply a sufficient quantity of oxygen for combustion, the heart represents the engine and pump, and various intricate chemical operations that go on are carried out in the laboratory, which consists of the kidneys and liver. Our arms and hands are like very powerful cranes and grabs for lifting or grasping things and moving them about